Enrich Blackline Masters
Grade 6

PROVIDES Daily Enrichment Activities

D1298064

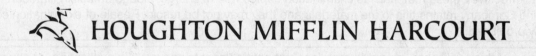

HOUGHTON MIFFLIN HARCOURT

Table of Contents

CRITICAL AREA: The Number System

Chapter 1: Whole Numbers and Decimals

Chapter 2: Fractions

Chapter 3: Rational Numbers

CRITICAL AREA: Ratios and Rates

Chapter 4: Ratios and Rates

Chapter 5: Percents

Chapter 6: Units of Measure

CRITICAL AREA: Expressions and Equations

Chapter 7: Algebra: Expressions

Chapter 8: Algebra: Equations and Inequalities

Chapter 9: Algebra: Relationships Between Variables

CRITICAL AREA: Geometry and Statistics

Chapter 10: Area

Chapter 11: Surface Area and Volume

Chapter 12: Data Displays and Measures of Center

Chapter 13: Variability and Data Distributions

Division Bugs

Scientists have discovered a new insect! Use the features of the new insect that are listed below to solve the problem. Write a division number sentence for each.

The insect has:

- 6 wings
- 15 legs
- 32 eyes
- 116 scales
- 213 hairs

1. A scientist found a colony of the new insects. If she counted 165 legs, how many insects are in the colony?

_____

_____

2. Dr. Wilburn is studying a group of insects. There are 2,784 scales in the group. How many insects are in Dr. Wilburn's group?

_____

_____

3. In a group of insects, there are 264 wings. How many insects are there?

_____

_____

4. Name the new insect and give it another feature (such as number of antennae). Write a division sentence using the insect's new feature.

_____

_____

5. Stretch Your Thinking Carla sees a group of insects. She counts 190 eyes. Is this possible? Explain.

_____

_____

_____

6. **Write Math** ▶ Explain how knowing simple multiplication facts can help you with division with greater numbers.

_____

_____

_____

Name _____

Symmetric Factor Trees

Both factor trees below show the prime factorization of 40.
The factor tree on the right is symmetric because both branches
have the same shape.

Not Symmetric

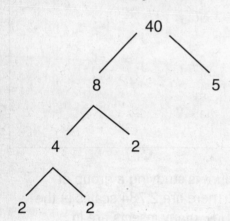

Symmetric

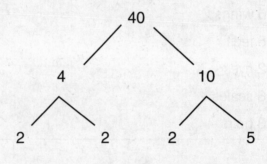

Create a symmetric factor tree for each number.

1. 90

2. 16

3. Stretch Your Thinking Create a
symmetric factor tree for a number that
has more than two prime factors and is
greater than 100.

4. | Write Math | ► Can you make a
symmetric factor tree for every
composite number? Explain.

_____

_____

_____

_____

Name _____

Mix and Match

In the table below, draw lines from each LCM in the first column to two numbers in the second column that share the LCM. Once a number in the right column is used, it cannot be used again.

Example:
    LCM: 12   Numbers: 3 and 4

	LCM	Numbers
1.	12	3
		4
2.	18	6
		9
3.	42	14
		15
4.	60	16
		18
5.	72	20
		21
6.	160	22
		24
7.	176	32
		40

8. Stretch Your Thinking Put together a new pair of numbers from the table, whose LCM is not in the table. Write the numbers and the LCM.

_____

_____

Name _____

Greatest Common Factor Match

Match the set of numbers inside each large triangle with its greatest
common factor inside a small triangle.

1.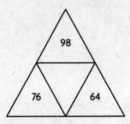

2.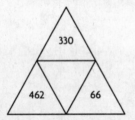

3.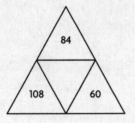

4.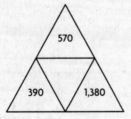

5. **Write Math** ▶ Explain how you found the greatest common factor
for three numbers.

_____

_____

_____

_____

Shelving Fun

The Mega-Super-Mart gets shipments of all kinds of products every day. Unpack the shipping boxes and put the products in the bins. Make sure to only put one kind of product in each bin and put the same number of items in each bin. The bins should also hold the greatest number of items possible.

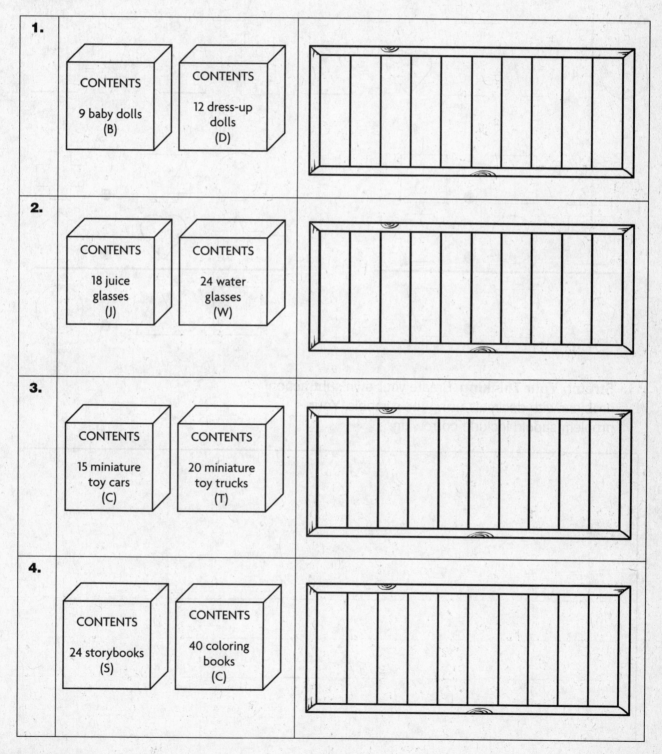

1.

CONTENTS

9 baby dolls
(B)

CONTENTS

12 dress-up dolls
(D)

2.

CONTENTS

18 juice glasses
(J)

CONTENTS

24 water glasses
(W)

3.

CONTENTS

15 miniature toy cars
(C)

CONTENTS

20 miniature toy trucks
(T)

4.

CONTENTS

24 storybooks
(S)

CONTENTS

40 coloring books
(C)

Digit Logic

Each symbol stands for a different digit from 0–9. The dark dots represent decimal points. Use the addition and subtraction problems to discover which digit is represented by each symbol.

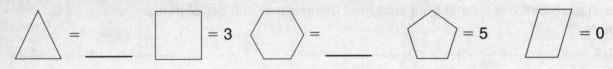

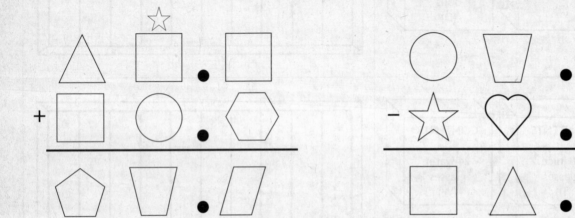

1. **Stretch Your Thinking** Create your own subtraction problem with decimals using the symbols. Your problem should include borrowing.

Place the Decimal Point

**Each answer shows the decimal point in the wrong place.
Estimate each product. Then make sure the decimal point is
put in the correct place.**

1. 1.6
     × 0.9
     ———
     14.4   **Estimate:** _____

                     Correct answer: _____

2. 4.6
     × 3.2
     ———
     147.2   **Estimate:** _____

                     Correct answer: _____

3. 2.7
     × 18.1
     ———
     4.887   **Estimate:** _____

                     Correct answer: _____

4. 9.6
     ×14.7
     ———
     1,411.2   **Estimate:** _____

                     Correct answer: _____

5. 0.9
     × 57.9
     ———
     5.211   **Estimate:** _____

                     Correct answer: _____

6. 0.75
     × 4.22
     ———
     316.5   **Estimate:** _____

                     Correct answer: _____

7. 34.5
     × 12.2
     ———
     42.09   **Estimate:** _____

                     Correct answer: _____

8. 28.8
     × 15.5
     ———
     4.464   **Estimate:** _____

                     Correct answer: _____

Write Math ➤ How can estimating the product help you place the
decimal point?

_____

_____

_____

_____

Decimal Match-Up

Draw lines to match each expression in the left column to
a value in the right column.

1.	$169.12 \div 14$		39.7
2.	$186.24 \div 12$		16.08
3.	$158.8 \div 4$		147.156
4.	$122.23 \div 17$		12.08
5.	$385.92 \div 24$		24.03
6.	$(300 - 100.9) \div 10$		3.94
7.	$(189.6 + 74.73) \div 11$		15.52
8.	$102.756 + (710.4 \div 16)$		8.88
9.	$122.14 \div 31$		7.19
10.	$781.44 \div 88$		19.91

Find the Decimal Point

Circle the correct answer without actually dividing.

1. 3.45 ÷ 0.5 =
    6.9
    0.69
    0.069

2. 1.52 ÷ 0.08 =
    19
    1.9
    0.19

3. 1.08 ÷ 1.8 =
    6.0
    0.6
    0.06

4. 2.3 ÷ 0.23 =
    100
    10
    0.1

5. 0.009 ÷ 0.1 =
    9
    0.9
    0.09

6. 2.004 ÷ 0.02 =
    100.2
    10.2
    1.2

7. 30.6 ÷ 0.006 =
    51,000
    5,100
    510

8. 2.004 ÷ 0.0005 =
    4,008
    408
    48

9. 50.26 ÷ 2 =
    251.3
    25.13
    2.513

10. 0.00006 ÷ 0.3 =
    2
    0.002
    0.0002

11. 64.028 ÷ 0.4 =
    16,007
    1,600.7
    160.07

12. 4.1 ÷ 2.05 =
    20
    2
    0.2

13. 480.3 ÷ 0.03 =
    161,000
    160,100
    16,010

14. 5 ÷ 0.0001 =
    500,000
    50,000
    5,000

15. How many times should you move the decimal point
in the dividend if the divisor is 0.000000009?

_____

16. Stretch Your Thinking If the dividend is a whole number and the divisor is 3.68,
how do you move the decimal point for the dividend?

_____

_____

_____

Repeat, Repeat, Repeat

Every fraction can be written as a terminating or repeating decimal by dividing the numerator by the denominator until the quotient terminates or starts repeating. For a repeating decimal, write a bar above the digit or digits that repeat.

Write each fraction as a repeating decimal.

1. $\frac{7}{9}$	2. $\frac{2}{7}$	3. $\frac{8}{11}$
_____	_____	_____
4. $\frac{2}{13}$	5. $\frac{6}{7}$	6. $\frac{3}{14}$
_____	_____	_____
7. $\frac{2}{6}$	8. $\frac{8}{12}$	9. $\frac{4}{9}$
_____	_____	_____

10. **Stretch Your Thinking** Write repeating decimals for the fractions $\frac{1}{11}$, $\frac{2}{11}$, and $\frac{3}{11}$. Find a pattern that you can use to write $\frac{4}{11}$ as a repeating decimal.

_____

_____

11. **Stretch Your Thinking** Write repeating decimals for $\frac{1}{9}$, $\frac{1}{99}$, and $\frac{1}{999}$. What do you think is the repeating decimal for $\frac{1}{9,999}$?

_____

_____

Choose the Right Path

Find the path from $\frac{1}{4}$ to 3.1 in order from least to greatest.
Start at $\frac{1}{4}$ and end at 3.1.

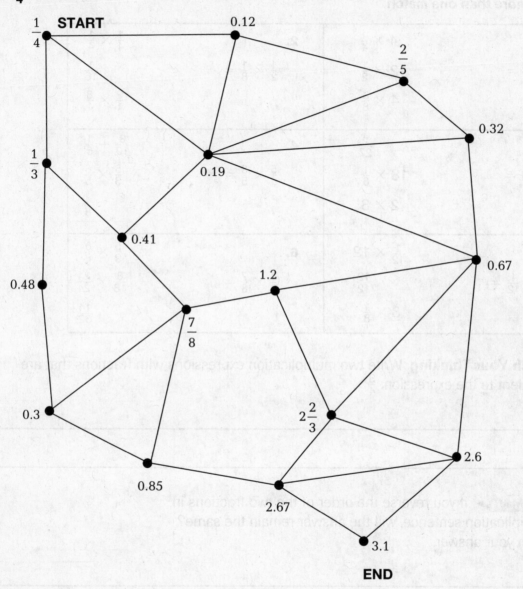

1. **Stretch Your Thinking** Find a different path through the maze by changing some of the numbers.

2. **Write Math** ▸ Explain how you found the answer to the problem you wrote.

_____

_____

_____

Multiplication Expression Match

Draw a line to match the multiplication expression on the left to
an equivalent expression or fraction on the right. Some expressions
will have more than one match.

1.		2.	
	$4 \times \frac{1}{4}$		$\frac{1}{4} \times \frac{1}{4}$
$8 \times \frac{3}{4} =$	$12 \times \frac{1}{2}$	$\frac{1}{2} \times \frac{1}{8} =$	$\frac{1}{16}$
	$4 \times \frac{3}{8}$		$\frac{2}{1} \times \frac{8}{1}$
3.		4.	
	$\frac{2}{27}$		$\frac{3}{10} + \frac{1}{5}$
$\frac{2}{3} \times 9 =$	$18 \times \frac{1}{6}$	$\frac{5}{6} \times \frac{3}{5} =$	$\frac{5}{3} \times \frac{6}{5}$
	2×3		$\frac{4}{8}$
5.		6.	
	$\frac{1}{12} \times 12$		$\frac{5}{9} \times \frac{6}{8}$
$12 \times \frac{1}{12} =$	$\frac{12}{12}$	$\frac{4}{9} \times \frac{7}{8} =$	$\frac{8}{18} \times \frac{21}{24}$
	$8 \times \frac{1}{8}$		$\frac{14}{32}$

7. **Stretch Your Thinking** Write two multiplication expressions with fractions that are
equivalent to the expression: $\frac{3}{4} \times \frac{2}{3}$.

_____

_____

8. **Write Math** ▶ If you reverse the order of the two fractions in
a multiplication sentence, will the answer remain the same?
Explain your answer.

_____

_____

_____

_____

Matching Products

Match each multiplication expression on the left with its corresponding product on the right.

1. $\frac{3}{5} \times \frac{8}{9} \times \frac{1}{3}$ $\frac{1}{4}$

2. $\frac{1}{4} \times \frac{9}{10} \times \frac{2}{3}$ $\frac{6}{13}$

3. $\frac{5}{7} \times \frac{2}{5} \times \frac{7}{8}$ $\frac{8}{45}$

4. $\frac{5}{8} \times \frac{7}{10} \times \frac{4}{5}$ $\frac{7}{20}$

5. $\frac{3}{14} \times \frac{7}{9} \times \frac{1}{6}$ $\frac{5}{18}$

6. $\frac{5}{12} \times \frac{3}{4} \times \frac{8}{9}$ $\frac{3}{20}$

7. $\frac{6}{7} \times \frac{9}{10} \times \frac{7}{12}$ $\frac{1}{36}$

8. $\frac{2}{3} \times \frac{12}{13} \times \frac{3}{4}$ $\frac{7}{100}$

9. $\frac{2}{5} \times \frac{7}{8} \times \frac{1}{5}$ $\frac{2}{45}$

10. $\frac{3}{4} \times \frac{4}{9} \times \frac{2}{15}$ $\frac{9}{20}$

Fraction Division Grids

Draw a fraction strip model to show the quotient for the
division expression. Then, in the grid above the expression,
find three squares in a row, column, or diagonal that have the
same quotient. Circle that row, column, or diagonal.

1.

$10 \div \frac{1}{2}$	$\frac{1}{5} \div 2$	$3 \div \frac{3}{8}$
$\frac{3}{4} \div \frac{1}{8}$	$1 \div \frac{1}{8}$	$2 \div \frac{1}{8}$
$4 \div \frac{1}{2}$	$2 \div \frac{1}{2}$	$\frac{3}{4} \div \frac{3}{8}$

$2 \div \frac{1}{4}$

2.

$\frac{1}{2} \div 9$	$12 \div 2$	$2 \div 6$
$3 \div \frac{1}{6}$	$3 \div \frac{1}{2}$	$4 \div 3$
$\frac{3}{4} \div 9$	$\frac{1}{3} \div 4$	$\frac{1}{4} \div 3$

$\frac{1}{2} \div 6$

3.

$1 \div \frac{1}{5}$	$\frac{4}{5} \div \frac{2}{5}$	$\frac{1}{2} \div \frac{1}{8}$
$\frac{8}{5} \div \frac{4}{5}$	$\frac{1}{2} \div \frac{1}{2}$	$3 \div \frac{3}{4}$
$\frac{1}{4} \div 2$	$\frac{8}{5} \div \frac{1}{10}$	$\frac{1}{3} \div \frac{1}{12}$

$\frac{4}{5} \div \frac{1}{5}$

4.

$1 \div \frac{1}{4}$	$\frac{5}{6} \div \frac{5}{12}$	$2 \div \frac{1}{3}$
$2 \div \frac{1}{4}$	$\frac{1}{4} \div \frac{1}{8}$	$1 \div \frac{1}{3}$
$4 \div 8$	$\frac{1}{2} \div \frac{1}{4}$	$\frac{3}{4} \div 2$

$\frac{3}{4} \div \frac{3}{8}$

5. Stretch Your Thinking Find the quotient $\frac{1}{4} \div 2\frac{1}{2}$. Draw a model. Explain how your model
represents the quotient.

_____

_____

_____

Name _____

Hidden Numbers

**Sarah estimated the quotient of each problem. What numbers
could be hiding in the problems? Fill in the blanks.**
Hint: There is more than one correct answer for each problem.

1. $5\frac{5}{6} \div$ _____

Estimated quotient: 3

2. $15\frac{5}{7} \div$ _____

Estimated quotient: 2

3. _____ $\div \frac{3}{7}$

Estimated quotient: 6

4. _____ $\div 5\frac{8}{10}$

Estimated quotient: 3

5. $19\frac{9}{11} \div$ _____

Estimated quotient: 5

6. $9\frac{2}{9} \div$ _____

Estimated quotient: 1

7. _____ $\div 1\frac{6}{7}$

Estimated quotient: 11

8. _____ $\div 3\frac{8}{10}$

Estimated quotient: 4

9. _____ $\div$ _____

Estimated quotient: $8 \div 4 = 2$

10. _____ $\div$ _____

Estimated quotient: $21 \div 7 = 3$

11. **Write Math** Why is it helpful to know how to estimate quotients?

_____

_____

12. **Write Math** Compare your problem solving method for problems with missing
dividends to your method for missing divisors.

_____

_____

_____

Funny Fractions

Find the quotient. Write the answer in simplest form.
Then match the letters from the boxes to the quotients
below to answer the riddle.

$\frac{3}{4} \div \frac{2}{3}$ E	$5 \div \frac{1}{4}$ C	$\frac{1}{10} \div \frac{5}{7}$ T
$\frac{7}{8} \div \frac{1}{4}$ Y	$\frac{4}{5} \div \frac{1}{3}$ I	$\frac{9}{10} \div \frac{3}{4}$ H
$\frac{3}{5} \div \frac{7}{10}$ N	$\frac{1}{6} \div \frac{5}{8}$ E	$8 \div \frac{2}{3}$ S
$\frac{1}{5} \div \frac{5}{6}$ D	$\frac{4}{9} \div \frac{2}{3}$ H	$\frac{1}{4} \div \frac{5}{8}$ A

Riddle:

What did the fraction say to its reciprocal during gymnastics class?

$$\underset{\frac{2}{3}}{\underline{\hspace{1.2cm}}} \ \underset{1\frac{1}{8}}{\underline{\hspace{1.2cm}}} \ \underset{3\frac{1}{2}}{\underline{\hspace{1.2cm}}} , \quad \underset{\frac{6}{7}}{\underline{\hspace{1.2cm}}} \ \underset{2\frac{2}{5}}{\underline{\hspace{1.2cm}}} \ \underset{20}{\underline{\hspace{1.2cm}}} \ \underset{\frac{4}{15}}{\underline{\hspace{1.2cm}}}$$

$$\underset{1\frac{1}{5}}{\underline{\hspace{1.2cm}}} \ \underset{\frac{4}{15}}{\underline{\hspace{1.2cm}}} \ \underset{\frac{2}{5}}{\underline{\hspace{1.2cm}}} \ \underset{\frac{6}{25}}{\underline{\hspace{1.2cm}}} \ \underset{12}{\underline{\hspace{1.2cm}}} \ \underset{\frac{7}{50}}{\underline{\hspace{1.2cm}}} \ \underset{\frac{2}{5}}{\underline{\hspace{1.2cm}}} \ \underset{\frac{6}{7}}{\underline{\hspace{1.2cm}}} \ \underset{\frac{6}{25}}{\underline{\hspace{1.2cm}}} !$$

Name _____

Party Food

Find out how many servings Alex and Keisha have of the pizza they plan to serve at their party. Draw a model to find the number of servings.

1. Cheese pizza Total: $2\frac{1}{4}$ pizzas Serving: $\frac{5}{16}$ pizza	$2\frac{1}{4} \div \frac{5}{16} =$ _____ **How many $\frac{5}{16}$-pizza servings are in $2\frac{1}{4}$ pizzas?** _____ with _____ serving left over
2. Pepperoni pizza Total: $2\frac{7}{8}$ pizzas Serving: $\frac{5}{16}$ pizza	$2\frac{7}{8} \div \frac{5}{16} =$ _____ **How many $\frac{5}{16}$-pizza servings are in $2\frac{7}{8}$ pizzas?** _____ with _____ serving left over

3. What is the greatest number of people Alex and Keisha can have at their party so that each person receives a serving of pizza?

4. Suppose each person at the party will eat one serving of cheese pizza and one serving of pepperoni pizza. Use the number from Problem 3 to find the serving size Alex and Keisha need to divide each pizza into.

_____   _____

Name _____

Mixed Number Division Balloons

In the balloon above the dividend, write the number of the correct
quotient from the list on the bottom. In the balloon above the divisor,
write the letter of its reciprocal from the right column.

Division Balloons   **Reciprocals**

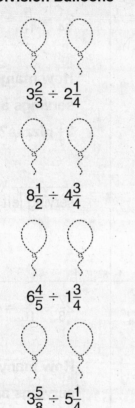

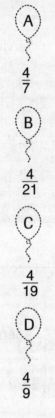

$3\frac{2}{3} \div 2\frac{1}{4}$ A $\frac{4}{7}$

$8\frac{1}{2} \div 4\frac{3}{4}$ B $\frac{4}{21}$

$6\frac{4}{5} \div 1\frac{3}{4}$ C $\frac{4}{19}$

$3\frac{5}{8} \div 5\frac{1}{4}$ D $\frac{4}{9}$

(1) $1\frac{15}{19}$ (2) $8\frac{1}{4}$ (3) $\frac{29}{42}$ (4) $3\frac{31}{35}$ (5) $1\frac{17}{27}$ (6) $1\frac{31}{36}$

1. Write $6\frac{11}{12} \div 7\frac{6}{11}$ as a multiplication expression using fractions greater
than 1. How can you simplify the expression?

_____

2. **Write Math** ▸ Write the steps for dividing two mixed numbers.

_____

_____

_____

Now Arriving, Flight 5 $\frac{2}{3}$ ...

The table below shows flight times and distances from San Francisco International Airport to other airports. Answer the questions that follow. Write your answers as fractions in simplest form.

San Francisco International Airport			
Destination	Departure (Leaves)	Arrival (San Francisco Time)	Distance
San Diego, CA	8:30 A.M.	12:00 P.M.	525 mi
Portland, OR	9:45 A.M.	12:00 P.M.	638 mi
Santa Fe, NM	10:00 A.M.	3:20 P.M.	1,200 mi
San Antonio, TX	10:10 A.M.	5:20 P.M.	1,793 mi
Atlanta, GA	2:15 P.M.	10:00 P.M.	2,465 mi

1. What is the travel time for a flight from San Francisco to Santa Fe?

_____

2. How many hours longer is a flight to San Antonio than a flight to Portland?

_____

3. How many times longer (by hours) is a flight to Atlanta than a flight to San Diego?

_____

4. How many hours longer is a flight to San Diego than a flight to Portland?

_____

5. How many times longer (by hours) is a flight to Atlanta than a flight to Santa Fe?

_____

6. The airline has six flights per day to Portland. How many total hours does the airline fly to Portland?

_____

7. An airline determines its rates by charging $\frac{1}{5}$ of a dollar per mile. How much do flights to San Diego and Atlanta cost?

_____

_____

_____

8. Write Math ▶ Explain how to write 2 hours and 20 minutes as a mixed number.

_____

_____

_____

Riddling Integers

Graph the number. Write the given letter above the point.
Answer the riddle by copying the letters in order from left to right.

What did the positive number say to its opposite?

opposite of ⁻3	opposite of ⁻7	opposite of 8	opposite of ⁻1	opposite of ⁻6
E	T	O	O	A
opposite of 10	opposite of ⁻9	opposite of 5	⁻(⁻10)	⁻(⁻2)
D	V	T	E	N
opposite of 4	⁻(⁻5)	opposite of 2	opposite of the sum of 0.4 and 5.6	
B	G	S	N	
opposite of the difference of 6.8 and 3.8		opposite of the opposite of the sum of 3.3 and 4.7		
E		I		

⁻10   0   10

__ __ __ ' __ __ __ __ __ __ __ __ __ __ __ __!

What did the negative number reply?

opposite of 4	opposite of ⁻2	opposite of ⁻9	opposite of ⁻7	opposite of 6
M	Y	H	T	V
opposite of ⁻8	opposite of 3	⁻(⁻5)	opposite of 5	⁻(⁻4)
C	E	A	E	M
opposite of 0	⁻(⁻1)	opposite of the sum of 2.3, 5.4, 1.2, and 0.1		
T	M	I		

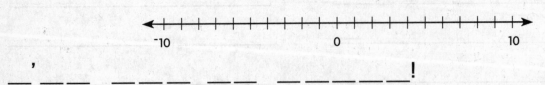

⁻10   0   10

__ , __ __ __ __ __ __ __ __ __ __!

Climb the Ladder

Jacob and Katya draw cards with positive and negative integers. In each round, the player with the greater integer moves up one space on the ladder.

Record the result of each round as R1, R2, R3, etc. on each player's ladder on the right. The first round has been done for you.

Round	Jacob's card	Katya's card
R1	5	⁻4
R2	⁻12	10
R3	⁻1	⁻2
R4	20	⁻13
R5	5	1
R6	⁻3	1
R7	⁻4	2
R8	9	⁻15
R9	⁻8	⁻18
R10	⁻7	11

Jacob	Katya
R1	

START

1. The person closet to the top is the winner. Who won the game? _____

2. **Write Math** ▶ Suppose Jacob and Katya had to find the opposite of their integers before deciding the winner of the round. Explain how this would change the winner of each round and the winner of the game.

_____

_____

_____

Rational Mix-Ups

Match the number on the right to the number line on the left that shows the two integers the number is between.

Then write A or B to tell which point on the number line is closer to the rational number.

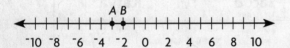

$\dfrac{7}{15}$ _____

-2.99 _____

-8.25 _____

$-5\dfrac{9}{10}$ _____

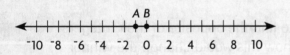

$8\dfrac{1}{7}$ _____

$\dfrac{8}{3}$ _____

-0.4 _____

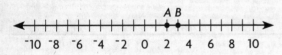

$\dfrac{23}{4}$ _____

1. Stretch Your Thinking Name a rational number between -1 and -2.

Is your number closer to -1 or -2?

Rational Comparisons

**Compare the numbers. Then name a number
that is between them in value.**

1. $^-5.3$ ◯ $^-4\frac{9}{10}$

_____

2. $^-\frac{1}{5}$ ◯ $^-0.3$

_____

3. $^-2\frac{4}{5}$ ◯ $^-2\frac{1}{2}$

_____

4. $^-\frac{7}{5}$ ◯ $^-1.1$

_____

5. 0.25 ◯ $^-0.1$

_____

6. $^-3\frac{2}{5}$ ◯ $^-3.6$

_____

7. $^-4\frac{3}{4}$ ◯ $^-4.7$

_____

8. $^-\frac{1}{8}$ ◯ $^-\frac{2}{5}$

_____

9. **Write Math** ▸ What steps did you use to solve Problem 2?

_____

_____

_____

_____

Mountain Climbing

The Eagle Mountain Campground offers hikers a chart of the elevations of various park sites in relation to the campground.

Crystal Lake has an elevation of ⁻60 feet in relation to the campground. Write and simplify and expression to find how far each site is above Crystal Lake.

Site	Elevation	Distance Above Crystal Lake
Hillside Overlook	20 feet	$|^-60| + |20| =$ _____ feet
Granite Cliffs	125 feet	_____ feet
Pinetree Glen	51 feet	_____ feet
Forester's Cabin	96 feet	_____ feet
Snowy Peaks	111 feet	_____ feet
Canopy Forest	60 feet	_____ feet

1. What is the difference in elevation between Hillside Overlook and Forester's Cabin?

_____

2. What site's elevation above Crystal Lake is the same as Snowy Peaks' elevation from the campgroud?

_____

3. The bait and tackle shop has an elevation of ⁻47 feet in relation to the campground. What is the difference in elevation between Crystal Lake and the bait and tackle shop?

_____

4. **Write Math** ▷ Explain how you found your answer to Problem 3.

_____

_____

_____

_____

It's Colder Than You Think

When it gets chilly, wind makes it feel even colder than the actual temperature on the thermometer. Use the wind chill chart and absolute value to answer the questions.

	Actual Temperature						
	30°F	20°F	10°F	0°F	⁻10°F	⁻20°F	⁻30°F
Wind Speed	Temperature with Wind Chill						
5 mph	25°F	13°F	1°F	⁻11°F	⁻22°F	⁻34°F	⁻46°F
10 mph	21°F	9°F	⁻4°F	⁻16°F	⁻28°F	⁻41°F	⁻53°F
15 mph	19°F	6°F	⁻7°F	⁻19°F	⁻32°F	⁻45°F	⁻58°F
20 mph	17°F	4°F	⁻9°F	⁻22°F	⁻35°F	⁻48°F	⁻61°F

1. How cold does it feel when the actual temperature is 20°F and the wind speed is 15 mph?

_____

2. For what wind speed does an actual temperature of ⁻30°F feel like ⁻61°F?

_____

3. With a wind speed of 5 mph, how much colder does it feel if the actual temperature is 10°F than if it is 30°F?

_____

4. If the actual temperature is ⁻10°F, how much colder does it feel with a wind speed of 10 mph?

_____

5. With a wind speed of 15 mph, how much colder does it feel if the actual temperature is ⁻20°F than if it is ⁻10°F?

_____

6. If the actual temperature is 10°F, how much colder does it feel with a wind speed of 20 mph than with a wind speed of 5 mph?

_____

7. **Write Math** ▶ What steps did you use to answer Problem 6?

_____

_____

_____

Coordinate Plane Graphing Riddle

Graph each of the ordered pairs on the coordinate plane below.
Then connect points 1–14 in the order that you plotted them.
Finally, connect points 14 and 1 to answer the riddle.

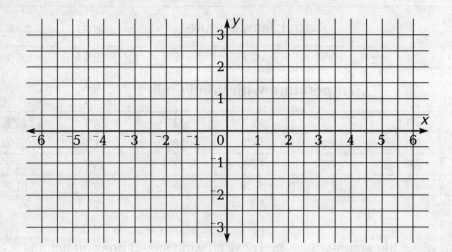

1. Z ($^-$5, 1.5)	2. A ($^-$4, 1)	3. D ($^-$2, 1.5)
4. A ($^-$1.5, ,3)	5. P (1, 1.5)	6. R (4.5, 1)
7. C (5, 0.5)	8. K (4.5, $^-$0.5)	9. S (5, $^-$1)
10. H (2.5, $^-$1.5)	11. J (1, $^-$2)	12. A (1, $^-$1)
13. B ($^-$4, $^-$0.5)	14. R ($^-$5, $^-$1.5)	15. K (4, 0.5) (This is a separate point.)

Riddle: What animal can you see at the bottom of the ocean?

_____

Hint: After you've connected points 1–14, take the letters from the question
numbers that are multiples of either 2 or 3 to spell out the answer.

Quadrant Detective

For each point, the absolute values of an ordered pair are given. Use the quadrant number to tell you if the *x*-coordinate and *y*-coordinate values are positive or negative. Then graph the point.

Point S Quadrant IV	Absolute values: (3, 7) Ordered pair: _____	**Point I** Quadrant II	Absolute values: (6, 2) Ordered pair: _____
Point E Quadrant III	Absolute values: (7, 6) Ordered pair: _____	**Point C** Quadrant I	Absolute values: (5, 1) Ordered pair: _____
Point R Quadrant II	Absolute values: (8, 6) Ordered pair: _____	**Point K** Quadrant IV	Absolute values: (8, 3) Ordered pair: _____
Point A Quadrant I	Absolute values: (2, 9) Ordered pair: _____	**Point T** Quadrant II	Absolute values: (4, 4) Ordered pair: _____
Point O Quadrant III	Absolute values: (2, 3) Ordered pair: _____	**Point H** Quadrant IV	Absolute values: (2, 1) Ordered pair: _____

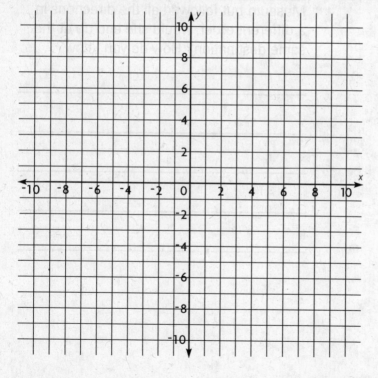

Read the graph top to bottom and left to right to spell a word.

_ _ _ _ _ _ _ _ _ _

Around Town

Natalie, Stefan, and Pilar are traveling around the city shown on the map. Give coordinates for their starting points, the points they pass through, and their destinations. Name their destinations. Trace the paths on the map.

Natalie starts at the Museum.	Stefan starts at the Library.	Pilar starts at the Bank.
Starting point: _____	Starting point: _____	Starting point: _____
East 8: _____	South 15: _____	West 3: _____
South 9: _____	West 6: _____	North 6: _____
East 4: _____	North 1: _____	East 5: _____
North 6: _____	West 5: _____	South 11: _____
Destination: _____	Destination: _____	East 6: _____
		Destination: _____

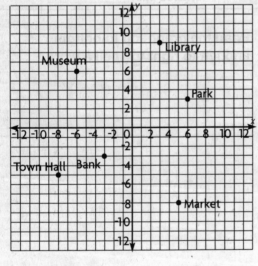

1. **Write Math** ▶ If Natalie started at the Museum but followed all the directions in a different order, would she end up at the same destination? How do you know?

_____

_____

_____

_____

_____

On the Slopes

Alyssa, Tabor, Ben, and Helena are on a skiing trip. At noon, one friend is skiing down the beginner slope, one is skiing down the expert (steeper) slope, one is hiking up the beginner slope, and one is taking the chair lift up the expert slope.

Given the x-coordinates, find the y-coordinates for each friend and graph the points. Draw a line connecting the points, and then tell what each friend is doing at noon.

Lines that go up from left to right are "uphill" slopes.
Lines that go down from left to right are "downhill" slopes.

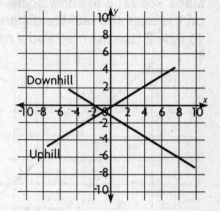

Ben

Moving up
1 unit and
right 2 units

x	y
0	0
2	
6	

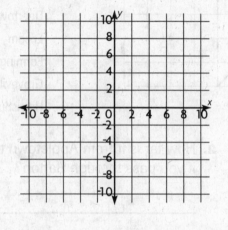

Tabor

Moving down
1 unit and
right 4 units

x	y
0	2
4	
8	

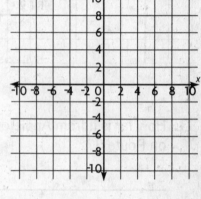

Alyssa

Moving down
1 unit and
right 2 units

x	y
0	1
2	
4	

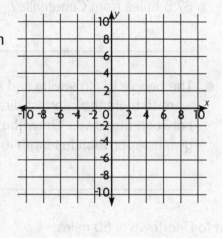

Helena

Moving up
1 unit and
right 4 units

x	y
⁻1	0
3	
7	

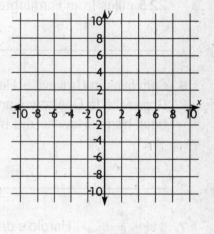

Down the beginner slope: _____   Down the expert slope: _____

Up the beginner slope: _____   Up the expert slope: _____

Ratio and Scale

Maps use ratio to show scale, the relationship between distance on the map and real-life distance. On this map, 1 inch represents 15 miles. Use the map and a ruler to answer the questions.

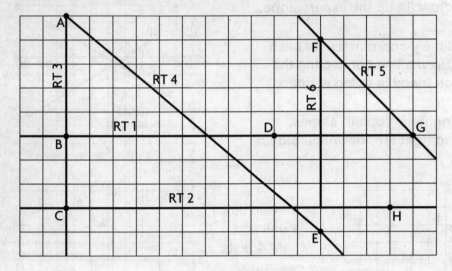

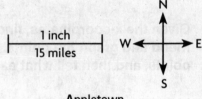

Appletown
Barton
Centerville
Deertown
Epsom
Farmington
Groveville
Harrisburg

1. How far is it from Appletown to Centerville on Route 3?

_____

2. How far is it from Appletown to Groveville if you pass through Barton?

_____

3. What town could you reach by driving 22.5 miles from Farmington?

_____

4. What town could you reach by driving 67.5 miles from Centerville?

_____

5. Sam lives in Groveville. He drove from Groveville to Deertown, and then drove back home. How far did he drive?

_____

6. The people of Groveville and Harrisburg want to build the shortest direct road between the towns. Draw the road and give its approximate length in miles.

_____

7. **Write Math** ➤ Harold's drive from Centertown to Deertown is 60 miles. Becca's drive is only 45 miles. Describe each path using route numbers and north, south, east, and west directions.

Mini Carpentry

Nathan and Paige are building dollhouse furniture with the same
scale as the furniture in their house. To do this, they are using a ratio
of 1 inch for the doll's furniture to 8 inches for the full-size furniture.

The drawings show the measurements of the full-size furniture.
Fill in the measurements for the doll's furniture.

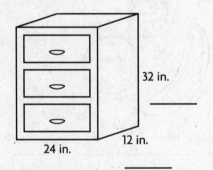

32 in. _____

24 in. 12 in.

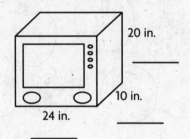

20 in. _____

10 in.

24 in. _____

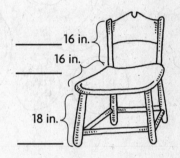

16 in. _____
16 in. _____

18 in. _____

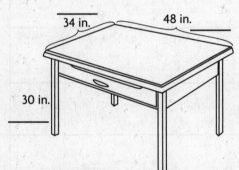

34 in. _____ 48 in. _____

30 in. _____

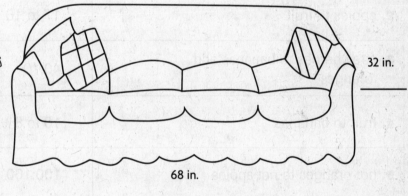

32 in. _____

68 in. _____

Write Math ▸ Explain how you can use a table to find the measurements for the doll's furniture.

_____

_____

_____

_____

Equivalent Fruit

Match each description with an equivalent ratio.

1. bananas to apples	$\dfrac{2}{10}$
2. apples to fruit	17 to 16
3. strawberries to bananas and oranges	40:10
4. fruit to bananas	10 to 8
5. not oranges to not apples	100:100

6. Write Math ▶ One math class has a greater number of students than the other. However, both classes have a ratio of 5 boys to 6 girls. How is this possible? Give an example.

_____

_____

_____

_____

Lots of Energy

Chase is preparing for a weekend group hike. Some parts of his recipes are missing. Make tables of equivalent ratios. Then complete the recipe.

1. Chase is making energy bars that contain sunflower seeds, rolled oats, and dried fruit. The ratio of sunflower seeds to rolled oats is 1:2. The ratio of sunflower seeds to dried fruit is 2:3.

ENERGY BARS RECIPE

4 cups sunflower seeds

_____ cups rolled oats

_____ cups dried fruit

1 cup almonds

0.5 cup honey

Sunflower seeds (cups)	1			
Rolled oats (cups)	2			

Sunflower seeds (cups)	2			
Dried fruit (cups)	3			

2. Chase is also making an energy drink that contains water, lemonade, and protein powder. The ratio of water to lemonade is 2:2.5. The ratio of water to protein powder is 8:1.

ENERGY DRINK RECIPE

16 cups water

_____ cups lemonade

_____ cups protein powder

Water (cups)	2			
Lemonade (cups)	2.5			

Water (cups)	8			
Protein powder (cups)	1			

3. **Write Math** ➤ Explain how you found the missing value for rolled oats in the first recipe.

_____

_____

_____

_____

Sunburst Ratios

Circle the value that makes an equivalent ratio.

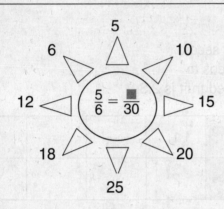

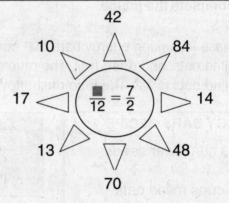

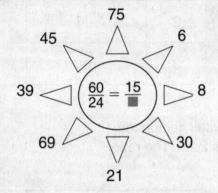

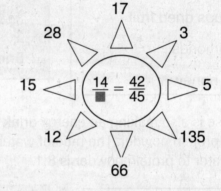

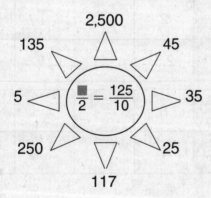

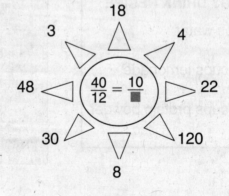

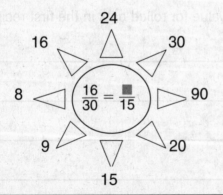

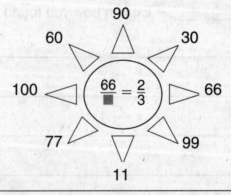

Matching Rates

Circle all the rates that are equivalent.

1. 340 pages in 20 days	**2.** 200 mi in 10 days
420 pages in 10 days	300 mi in 15 days
450 pages in 30 days	400 mi in 25 days
210 pages in 5 days	500 mi in 30 days
3. 128 jumps in 6 hr	**4.** 320 items in 5 pkg
256 jumps in 18 hr	212 items in 4 pkg
256 jumps in 12 hr	108 items in 2 pkg
16 jumps in 1 hr	159 items in 3 pkg
5. 120 countries in 3 days	**6.** 60 mi in 2 hr
23 countries in 2 days	180 mi in 3 hr
15 countries in 1 day	90 mi in 3 hr
46 countries in 4 days	120 mi in 4 hr
7. 12 problems in 2 min	**8.** 42 mi on 3 gal
15 problems in 3 min	58 mi on 2 gal
16 problems in 4 min	51 mi on 3 gal
20 problems in 5 min	87 mi on 3 gal
9. 80 apples in 10 sec	**10.** 11 hops in 15 sec
48 apples in 6 sec	66 hops in 30 sec
96 apples in 12 sec	88 hops in 120 sec
8 apples in 1 sec	22 hops in 20 sec
11. 155 ft in 5 hrs	**12.** 6 yd in 2 days
93 ft in 3 hrs	15 yd in 3 days
31 ft in 1 hr	105 yd in 21 days
62 ft in 4 hrs	12 yd in 3 days
13. 105 jacks in 3 bags	**14.** 768 revolutions in 12 min
210 jacks in 6 bags	832 revolutions in 14 min
240 jacks in 8 bags	448 revolutions in 7 min
35 jacks in 1 bag	1,664 revolutions in 26 min

Where Are the Words?

Write a word problem using unit rates to go with the equivalent ratios.
Then find the unknown value.

1. _____

_____

_____

_____

_____

$\dfrac{\blacksquare}{72} = \dfrac{200}{25}$

$ _____

2. _____

_____

_____

_____

_____

$\dfrac{8}{160} = \dfrac{\blacksquare}{60}$

_____ days

3. _____

_____

_____

_____

_____

$\dfrac{10}{15} = \dfrac{18}{\blacksquare}$

_____ games

Read the Graph

Fill in the labels, and use the graph to find the unit rate. Then give
the ordered pairs for equivalent rates not shown on the graph.

1. Samantha's Rate for Origami Cranes

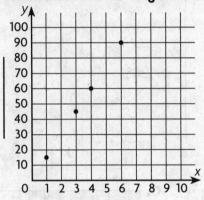

_____

Unit rate: _____

Ordered pairs: _____

2. Growth Rate for Josh's Pine Tree

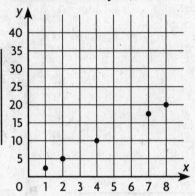

_____

Unit rate: _____

Ordered pairs: _____

3. Jamal's Driving Speed

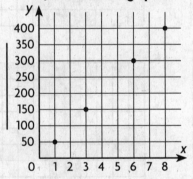

_____

Unit rate: _____

Ordered pairs: _____

4. Snowfall Rate

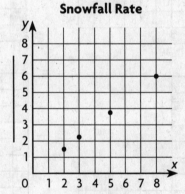

_____

Unit rate: _____

Ordered pairs: _____

5. **Write Math** ➤ How did you find the unit rate in Problem 3?

_____

_____

_____

Matching Models

Write the letter of the correct model for each ratio or percent.

1. 48%

_____

2. 70%

_____

3. $\frac{52}{100}$

_____

4. $\frac{30}{100}$

_____

5. $\frac{72}{100}$

_____

6. 36%

_____

A.

B.
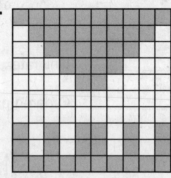

C.
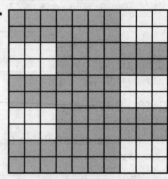

D.
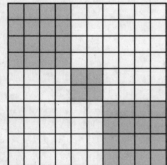

E.
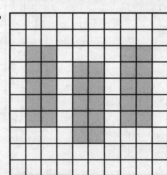

F.
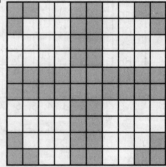

7. Stretch Your Thinking Describe how you could use one 10-by-10 grid to show that three different percents have a sum of 100%. Then shade the grid to show that 13% + 24% + 63% = 100%.

_____

_____

Percent Pictures

Follow the code to find the hidden picture.

0.9	$\frac{3}{5}$	$\frac{1}{4}$	0.06	$\frac{9}{10}$	0.66	0.32
1.50	5	0.5	$\frac{16}{32}$	$\frac{1}{2}$	0.77	4.5
0.04	$\frac{65}{77}$	$\frac{11}{22}$	$\frac{9}{20}$	$\frac{3}{6}$	0.06	$\frac{44}{100}$
$\frac{16}{31}$	$\frac{11}{100}$	0.500	$\frac{50}{100}$	0.50	0.14	$\frac{1}{5}$
$\frac{50}{120}$	0.12	$\frac{12}{25}$	0.4	$\frac{40}{60}$	0.004	0.88
$\frac{1}{1}$	0.400	1	$\frac{4}{10}$	0.03	$\frac{6}{15}$	$\frac{5}{6}$
0.07	6.5	$\frac{8}{20}$	$\frac{2}{5}$	$\frac{40}{100}$	0.99	0.43
0.29	0.045	$\frac{17}{20}$	0.40	0.730	0.83	$\frac{87}{100}$
$\frac{1}{7}$	0.15	$\frac{6}{23}$	0.58	$\frac{46}{100}$	0.91	1.11

1. Color numbers equivalent to 50% red.

2. Color numbers equivalent to 45% yellow.

3. Color numbers equivalent to 40% green.

What is the hidden picture?

_____

Name _____

Fraction, Decimal, Percent Soup

Use the fractions, decimals, percents, and ratios in the soup bowl
below to write the equivalent answers for each square. You will not
use all of the values in the bowl.

RATIO	FRACTION	RATIO	FRACTION	RATIO	FRACTION
4 out of 5	_____		$\frac{3}{8}$	_____	_____
				0.74	
_____	_____	_____	_____	_____	_____
DECIMAL	PERCENT	DECIMAL	PERCENT	DECIMAL	PERCENT
RATIO	FRACTION	RATIO	FRACTION	RATIO	FRACTION
26 out of 40	_____		_____	0.33 out of 100	_____
			142%		
_____	_____	_____		_____	_____
DECIMAL	PERCENT	DECIMAL	PERCENT	DECIMAL	PERCENT

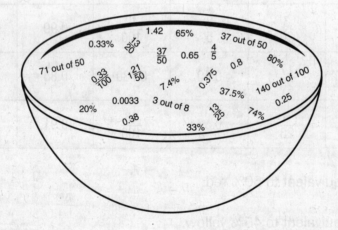

1. **Stretch Your Thinking** Write the
numbers and ratios that you did not
use in order from least to greatest.

_____

_____

_____

_____

2. **Write Math** ▸ Explain how to change
86% into an equivalent ratio written in
simplest form.

_____

_____

_____

_____

Percent Wheels

**Choose from the numbers below to complete the percent wheels.
The first one in Wheel 1 has been done for you.**

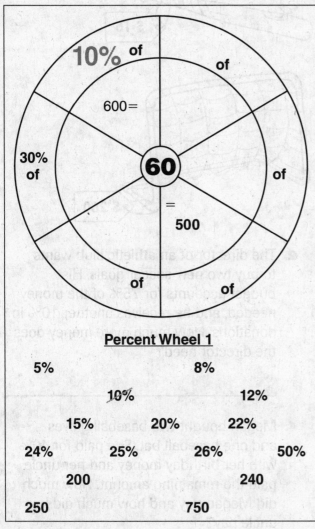

Percent Wheel 1

5%		8%
10%		12%
15%	20%	22%
24%	25%	26%	50%
200		240
250	750	

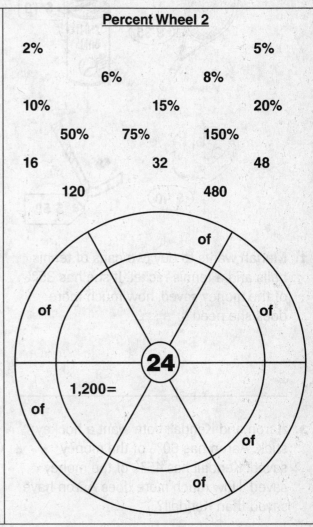

Percent Wheel 2

2%			5%
	6%	8%	
10%		15%	20%
50%	75%	150%	
16		32	48
120		480	

1. **Stretch Your Thinking** Write a percent problem where the answer is 80.

_____

_____

_____

_____

2. **Write Math** ▶ Is 150% of 25 equal to 25% of 150? Explain your answer.

_____

_____

_____

_____

Time to Shop!

Use the items in the sports store to solve the problems.

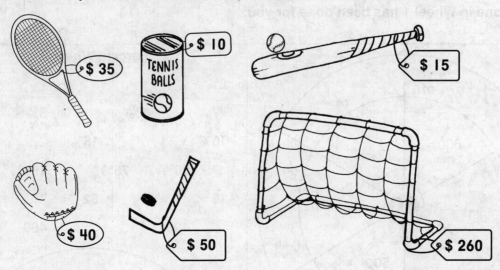

1. Mariah wants to buy two cans of tennis balls and a tennis racket. If she has 35% of the money saved, how much more does she need?

   _____

2. The director of an athletic club wants to buy two new soccer goals. His budget accounts for 75% of the money needed, and he receives another 10% in donations. How much more money does the director need?

   _____

3. Aaron and Kendall both want a hockey stick. Aaron has 60% of the money saved. Kendall has 45% of the money saved. How much more does Aaron have saved than Kendall?

   _____

4. Megan bought two baseball gloves and one baseball bat. She paid for 40% with her birthday money and her uncle paid the remaining amount. How much did Megan pay and how much did her uncle pay?

   _____

5. **Stretch Your Thinking** Describe a different method than the one you used to solve Problem 1.

   _____

   _____

   _____

   _____

A Whole Lotta Game

In a recreational basketball league, the Lions are playing the Bears.
The number of points scored from free throws and the percentage
of total points that are scored from free throws are given. Find the
total number of points scored in each quarter.

Lions		Bears	
1ST QUARTER	4 points is 25% of _____	1ST QUARTER	1 point is 10% of _____
2ND QUARTER	8 points is 40% of _____	2ND QUARTER	5 points is 20% of _____
3RD QUARTER	15 points is 50% of _____	3RD QUARTER	9 points is 45% of _____
4TH QUARTER	3 points is 20% of _____	4TH QUARTER	12 points is 75% of _____

1. How many total points did the Lions score? How many total points did the Bears score?

   _____

2. In basketball, the team with the most points wins the game. Which team won? By how many points?

   _____

3. **Write Math** ➤ Explain how to use multiplication instead of ratios to find the number of points the Lions scored in the 3rd quarter.

   _____

   _____

   _____

Name _____

Lotta Giga Nano

The metric system has linear units that are larger than a kilometer.
The metric system also has linear units that are smaller than a millimeter.
Some of them are given in the table below.

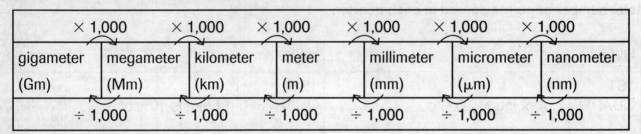

To convert from one unit to the next, multiply or divide by 1,000.

**Write *multiply* or *divide*. Decide how many times you multiply or divide
by 1,000 to convert to the given unit. Then find the value.**

1. 24 Mm = ▇ m

2. 458 μm = ▇ m

3. 5 km = ▇ m

4. 8 nm = ▇ m

5. 971 Gm = ▇ m

6. 12 nm = ▇ mm

7. 38 mm = ▇ km

8. 7 Gm = ▇ Mm

9. 795 nm = ▇ Mm

10. 156 km = ▇ m

Mixed Up Capacity

The measurements in the first column were converted to other units with the results in the second column. However, the rows got mixed up. Connect each measurement in the first column with its conversion in the second column.

Original Measurements	Converted Measurements
2 gal	6 pt
89 mL	56 cups
8 pt	8 qt
3 qt	35 gal
8.9 L	500 daL
28 pints	500 dL
89 hL	0.0089 kL
113 cups	904 fl oz
140 qt	8.9 kL
5 kL	0.89 dL
0.5 hL	1 gal

1. **Write Math** Explain how you could convert 152 cups to gallons.

_____

_____

_____

Name _____

Mixed Up Weight and Mass

The measurements in the first column were converted to other units with the results in the second column. However, the rows got mixed up. Connect each measurement in the first column with its conversion in the second column.

Original Measurements	Converted Measurements
4.6 hg	2.6 lb
0.56 lb	8.884 hg
41.6 oz	1.5 T
3,000 lb	4,600 dg
4.6 g	4,500 lb
128 oz	0.884 dag
88.4 dg	8.96 oz
2.25 T	4,600 mg
600,000 dag	6,000 lb
88,840 cg	6,000 kg
3 T	8 lb

1. **Write Math** ▸ Explain how you could convert $\frac{3}{4}$ ton to ounces.

_____

_____

_____

E46

Missing Pieces

For each problem, an answer is given. Fill in the blanks with numbers, units, or both.

1. $\dfrac{21\ L}{1\ hr} \times \boxed{\ \ } = 84\ L$

2. $\dfrac{36\ kg}{10\ hr} \times \dfrac{24\ hr}{1\ day} \times \boxed{\ \ }\ days = 259.2\ kg$

_____

3. $225\ sq\ m \div \boxed{\ \ } = 9\ m$

4. $\dfrac{18\ cm}{1\ min} \times \dfrac{1\ m}{100\ cm} \times \dfrac{60\ min}{1\ hr} \times \boxed{\ \ } = \dfrac{43.2\ m}{1\ hr}$

_____

5. $\dfrac{6\ gal}{1\ day} \times \dfrac{7\ days}{1\ week} \times \boxed{\ \ } = 168\ gal$

6. $108\ eeks \times \dfrac{1\ eep}{18\ eeks} \times \dfrac{1}{4\ eeps}\boxed{\ \ } = 1.5\ bleps$

_____

7. **Write Math** ▸ Explain how you solved Problem 6.

_____

_____

_____

_____

On Your Mark, Get Set, GO!!!!!

The car that travels farther wins. Name the car that wins each race.

Race #1 _____

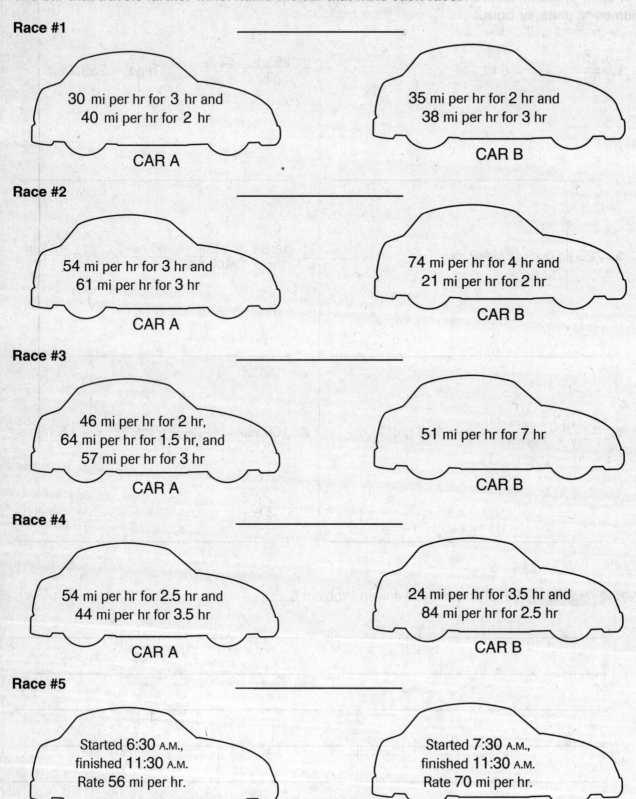

30 mi per hr for 3 hr and
40 mi per hr for 2 hr

CAR A

35 mi per hr for 2 hr and
38 mi per hr for 3 hr

CAR B

Race #2 _____

54 mi per hr for 3 hr and
61 mi per hr for 3 hr

CAR A

74 mi per hr for 4 hr and
21 mi per hr for 2 hr

CAR B

Race #3 _____

46 mi per hr for 2 hr,
64 mi per hr for 1.5 hr, and
57 mi per hr for 3 hr

CAR A

51 mi per hr for 7 hr

CAR B

Race #4 _____

54 mi per hr for 2.5 hr and
44 mi per hr for 3.5 hr

CAR A

24 mi per hr for 3.5 hr and
84 mi per hr for 2.5 hr

CAR B

Race #5 _____

Started 6:30 A.M.,
finished 11:30 A.M.
Rate 56 mi per hr.

CAR A

Started 7:30 A.M.,
finished 11:30 A.M.
Rate 70 mi per hr.

CAR B

Break the Exponent Bricks

Fill in the missing number to complete the number sentence.
Shade or cross out the answer in the bricks below to find the
route from the left to the right.

1. $3^{\underline{\quad}} = 2,187$	**2.** $\underline{\quad}^{7} = 0$	**3.** $6^{\underline{\quad}} = 1,296$
4. $2^{\underline{\quad}} = 256$	**5.** $4^{\underline{\quad}} = 4,096$	**6.** $\underline{\quad}^{1} = 9$
7. $2^9 = \underline{\quad}$	**8.** $\underline{\quad}^{2} = 64$	**9.** $7^{\underline{\quad}} = 343$
10. $1^{13} = \underline{\quad}$	**11.** $5^{\underline{\quad}} = 3,125$	**12.** $\underline{\quad}^{5} = 32$

Problem Number

	1	2	3	4	5	6	7	8	9	10	11	12
A	6	0	4	7	5	7	18	5	7	0	0	6
N	7	1	5	8	6	8	9	6	6	5	1	7
S	8	2	6	9	7	9	512	7	5	4	2	8
W	9	3	7	10	8	10	256	8	4	3	3	9
E	10	4	8	11	9	11	1,024	9	3	2	4	2
R	11	5	9	12	10	12	81	32	2	1	5	1

13. Stretch Your Thinking Write a number sentence with an exponent where the answer is one of the choices for Problem 7 that you did not cross out.

14. **Write Math** ▸ Is 6^4 equal to 4^6? Explain your answer.

_____

_____

_____

Order of Operations Game

Three players are playing a board game. Evaluate the expressions below. Move each player's piece the same number of spaces as the answers. Do not count the start space. Mark the space where each player's piece should be after 4 moves.

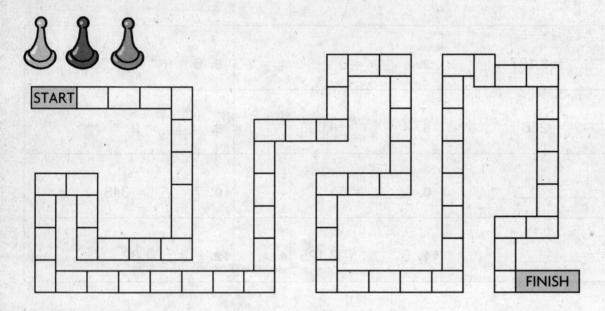

player 1	player 2	player 3
1. $(50 - 2) \div 2^2 =$ _____	**2.** $5 + 10 \div 5 =$ _____	**3.** $108 \div (3^3 - 9) =$ _____
4. $(7^3 - 5) \div (13^2) =$ _____	**5.** $(3 + 4) \div (1^1) =$ _____	**6.** $6^1 + 3 - 7 =$ _____
7. $(55 - 1^5) \div 9$ = _____	**8.** $(4^2 \times 3) \div (2^2 \times 6)$ = _____	**9.** $(8^2 \div 16) \times (11 - 6)$ = _____
10. $(15 - 6^2 \div 4) + (3^2 \times 2)$ = _____	**11.** $4^1 \times (8 + 51 \div 17)$ = _____	**12.** $12^2 - (10 + 4 \times 5^2)$ = _____

13. Stretch Your Thinking On his next move, player 1 is given an expression that moves his game piece directly to the finish space on the board. The expression has a division and a subtraction operation and an exponent. Write a possible expression.

_____

Which Expression Am I?

Match each word expression on the left with the correct algebraic expression on the right.

a number decreased by 9	$4n - 15$
9 times the sum of a number and 4	$n^3 + n$
15 less than 4 times a number	$n - 9$
the cube of a number increased by the number	$9n$
the product of a number and 9	$n^2 + 7n$
the square of a number, increased by the product of 7 and the number	$9(n + 4)$
the quotient of a number and 9	$\dfrac{n}{9} + 4$
4 times a number, increased by 15	$15 - 4n$
4 more than a number divided by 9	$9 - n$
a number increased by 9	$4n + 15$
15 decreased by 4 times a number	$\dfrac{n}{9}$
9 decreased by a number	$n + 9$

Tall Math Tales

Write sentences using words from the lists, choosing at least one phrase from each column. Then, for each sentence, create a math expression from the number or expression listed next to the phrases you chose. Finally, identify the number of terms in your expression.

For example, if you write "Oh no! The cow ate my blue pizza!" you might create the expression $4 + 6 \times (3n + 7) - 2n \times 3$.

Nouns		Verbs		Adjectives		Exclamations	
cow	6	sees	$(5n - 2)$	spotted	$5n$	Hooray!	7
elephant	12	ate	$(3n + 7)$	enormous	n	Oh no!	4
math book	5	became	$(12 - n)$	blue	$2n$	Wow!	9
pizza	3	sat	$(4n + 2)$	wooden	$4n$	Oops!	2
football	10	is carrying	n^2	shiny	$3n$	Whoops!	3
computer	4	caught	$2n^2$	delicious	$6n$	Yikes!	1

Sentence	Expression and Terms
1.	
2.	
3.	
4.	
5.	

Name _____

Round and Round They Go

Evaluate the expression for each value of *a*. Circle the correct answer.

$$8a - 2(3 + a)$$

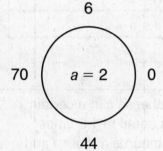

6   69   414

70   (*a* = 2)   0   132   (*a* = 3)   48   30   (*a* = 6)   288

44   12   144

$$3(a - 1)^2 + 2$$

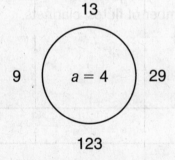
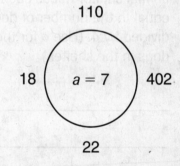

13   3   110

9   (*a* = 4)   29   7   (*a* = 2)   5   18   (*a* = 7)   402

123   27   22

$$5a - 3a + 11 - a^2$$

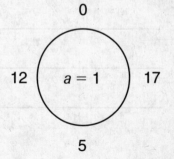

3   2   0

23   (*a* = 4)   35   3   (*a* = 3)   18   12   (*a* = 1)   17

7   8   5

Find the Formula

When an algebraic expression can be used in every example of
a certain situation, you can write an equation called a formula.
Formulas can have one, two, or more variables.

Examples

The area of a square is always equal to the square of the side length.	$A = s^2$
Distance is always equal to the product of rate and time.	$d = rt$

Write a formula for each situation.

1. The perimeter P of a rectangle is always equal to the sum of twice the length l and twice the width w.	**2.** The amount of cheese c in a certain recipe is always equal to 1.5 times the combined amounts of flour f and water w.
3. The number of bags of dog food a certain animal shelter needs each week is always equal to the number of dogs in the shelter divided by 4. (Use d for the number of dogs in the shelter.)	**4.** The number of violins in Amy's school orchestra is always equal to twice the combined number of flutes, clarinets, and bassoons.

5. ⬤ Write Math ▸ How did you choose variables to use in the last
two problems? Would the formulas give different results if you
chose different letters?

_____

_____

_____

Shaded Areas

**Write an expression for the area or perimeter of the figure.
Then combine like terms to simplify the expression.**

---

1. Find the area of the shaded region.

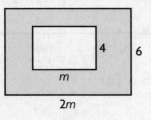

---

2. Find the area of the shaded region.

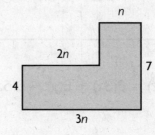

---

3. Find the perimeter.

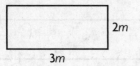

---

4. Find the perimeter.

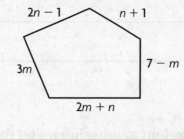

---

5. Write Math ▸ Describe how you wrote the expression for the shaded area in Problem 1.

_____

_____

_____

_____

_____

Powerful Properties

**Name the property or properties used to generate the
equivalent expression.**

1. $5b(ac) = 5(bac)$

_____

2. $(3s - 4) + (7t - s) = (7t - s) + (3s - 4)$

_____

3. $6(3x + y - 5z) = 6(3x) + 6(y) - 6(5z)$

_____

4. $(5 + 6x) + x = 5 + (6x + x)$

_____

5. $2(6x + 3 + x) = 2(6x + x + 3)$
$\qquad\qquad\quad = 2(6x + x) + 2(3)$

_____

_____

6. $y(2w) = 2wy$
$\qquad\quad = 2(wy)$

_____

_____

Write an equivalent expression using the property given.

7. $4(2 + a + b)$
Distributive Property

_____

_____

8. $(8m)(2)$
Commutative Property of Multiplication

_____

_____

9. **Write Math** ▸ Can you use the Commutative Property to justify that $3s - 4$ and
$4 - 3s$ are equivalent expressions? Explain.

_____

_____

_____

Name _____

Expression Secret Code

Find equivalent expressions to break the code and solve the riddle.

Riddle: What did one math book say to the other math book?

$3x$	2	$9 - x$	$8x + 9$	$10x - 5$	9	$5x + 8$
A	**B**	**C**	**D**	**E**	**F**	**G**
$x + 1$	$17x$	$10x - 10$	13	$16x$	$2x$	$8x - 10$
H	**I**	**J**	**K**	**L**	**M**	**N**
$17 - 5x$	$5x - 12$	$5 - 10x$	$4x$	$7x$	$12 - 15x$	$6x + 15$
O	**P**	**Q**	**R**	**S**	**T**	**U**
$15x$	10	$6x$	$x - 7$	$5x$		
V	**W**	**X**	**Y**	**Z**		

$5x + 12x$ $3(3x + 2x)$ $2x - 5 + 8x$ $6x - x + 8$ $7 - 5x + 10$

____   ____   ____   ____   ____

$3(4 - 5x)$ $2x + 3x - 12$ $2x + 2x$ $8 + 9 - 5x$ $8x + 2 - 8x$

____   ____   ____   ____

$4(x + 3x)$ $5x + 5x - 5$ $2x + (5x \cdot 0)$ $x + 4x + 2x$

____   ____   ____   ____!

Solution Matching

Match the equation with its solution.

1. $3 + x = 27$ $x = 40$

2. $42 = x - 14$ $x = 43$

3. $x + 6 = 19$ $x = 24$

4. $x - 37 = 3$ $x = 27$

5. $28 + x = 36$ $x = 35$

6. $x = 29 + 14$ $x = 56$

7. $25 - x = 18$ $x = 53$

8. $x + 15 = 42$ $x = 13$

9. $50 = x + 24$ $x = 7$

10. $48 - x = 13$ $x = 28$

11. $x - 32 = 21$ $x = 8$

12. $2x = 56$ $x = 9$

13. $36 - x = 4$ $x = 26$

14. $3x = 27$ $x = 32$

15. **Write Math** Explain how you made the first match.

_____

_____

_____

16. **Stretch Your Thinking** Explain how you could use mental math to find the solution to Problem 14.

_____

_____

Word Confusion

**Write the missing word, number, operation symbol, or variable
to make the word sentence match the equation.**

1. Three more than a number is _____.

$n +$ _____ $= 12$

2. _____ less than a number is 51.

n _____ $5 = 51$

3. Nine _____ a number is 81.

$9n =$ _____

4. The sum of a number and _____ is 39.8.

_____ $+ 24.8 =$ _____

5. The quotient of a number and _____ is 14.

n _____ $21 =$ _____

6. _____ less than a number is _____.

n _____ $11 = 24$

7. $3\frac{4}{5}$ is _____ more than a number.

_____ $= n + 1\frac{1}{2}$

8. 29.6 less than a _____ is _____.

n _____ $29.6 = 194.8$

9. A number increased by _____ is 24.

$n + 11 =$ _____

10. Fifteen is equal to _____ times a number.

_____ $= 7n$

11. The quotient of a _____ and 11 is 19.3.

$n \div$ _____ $= 19.3$

12. A number _____ by $7\frac{3}{4}$ is _____.

$n -$ _____ $= \frac{1}{2}$

13. The _____ of a number and 3.2 is 174.6.

$n \div$ _____ $=$ _____

14. A number _____ by 11.1 is _____.

$n -$ _____ $= 6.3$

15. Twice a number is _____.

_____ $n = 54$

16. When a number is _____ by 2.1, the result is 9.9.

$n + 2.1 =$ _____

17. Eleven _____ a number is 913.

$n -$ _____ $=$ _____

18. Twelve minus a _____ is 1.

_____ $- n =$ _____

Stay Balanced!

You learned that an equation must always stay balanced. For each equation, write a number in the box to keep it balanced.

1. $2 + 5 = \boxed{} + 1$

2. $4 + 4 = \boxed{} + 5$

3. $\boxed{} + 4 = 3 + 3$

4. $5 + \boxed{} = 1 + 4$

5. $11 + 4 = \boxed{} + 11$

6. $8 + 7 = 5 + \boxed{}$

7. $2 + \boxed{} = 15 - 9$

8. $5 + 6 = \boxed{} - 1$

9. $\boxed{} - 4 = 8 + 8$

10. $0 + \boxed{} = 14 - 6$

11. **Write Math** ▸ Explain how you balanced the equations.

_____

_____

_____

_____

Less Is More...and More Is Less

Circle the value of the variable that makes the equation true.

39 | $a + 4 = 35$ | 31   27 | $21 = b - 6$ | 15

2 | $c + 7 = 9$ | 16   9 | $5 = x - 4$ | 1

1.3 | $y - 4.1 = 5.4$ | 9.5   12.5 | $16.4 = c + 3.9$ | 20.3

$10\frac{1}{4}$ | $v + 3\frac{3}{4} = 14$ | $17\frac{3}{4}$ $2\frac{5}{6}$ | $5\frac{2}{3} = d - 2\frac{5}{6}$ | $8\frac{1}{2}$

$1\frac{4}{9}$ | $k - 2\frac{5}{9} = 4$ | $6\frac{5}{9}$ $13\frac{3}{4}$ | $12\frac{1}{4} = d + 1\frac{1}{2}$ | $10\frac{3}{4}$

15 | $b - 4 = 11$ | 7   43 | $30 = x + 13$ | 17

6 | $j + 32 = 38$ | 70   18 | $5 = x - 13$ | 8

Fractioned Tiles

Sharon wants to use algebra tiles to solve equations whose solutions are mixed numbers. She made algebra tiles out of cardboard so she could cut them in equal pieces. This is how she solved the equation below.

$$4x = 17 \qquad\qquad x = 4\tfrac{1}{4}$$

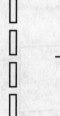  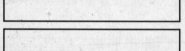

$4\tfrac{1}{4}$ per row

Solve each equation by drawing a model.

1. $3x = 19$ $\qquad\qquad\qquad x =$ _____

2. $4x = 30$ $\qquad\qquad\qquad x =$ _____

3. $6x = 49$ $\qquad\qquad\qquad x =$ _____

The Path Less Traveled

Solve the equation $\frac{r}{4} = 6$. Then follow the arrow at the solution to
the next equation. Keep doing this until you have solved each
equation. Show the path by giving the solution to each equation.
What letter did you form?

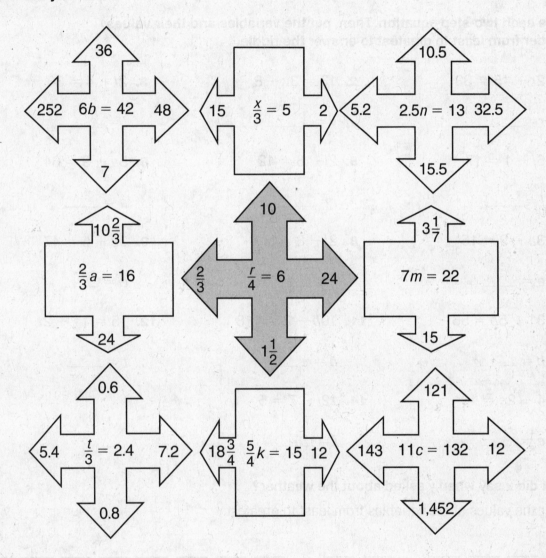

36

252    $6b = 42$ 48

7

10.5

15    $\frac{x}{3} = 5$ 2

5.2 $2.5n = 13$ 32.5

15.5

$10\frac{2}{3}$

$\frac{2}{3}a = 16$

24

10

$\frac{2}{3}$ $\frac{r}{4} = 6$ 24

$1\frac{1}{2}$

$3\frac{1}{7}$

$7m = 22$

15

0.6

5.4 $\frac{t}{3} = 2.4$ 7.2

0.8

$18\frac{3}{4}$ $\frac{5}{4}k = 15$ 12

121

143    $11c = 132$ 12

1,452

_____

_____

_____

Name _____

Do the Two-Step

To solve a two-step equation, first add or subtract a number from both sides to undo the subtraction or addition, creating a simpler equation. Then, solve the simpler equation by multiplying or dividing by a number on both sides to undo the division or multiplication.

Solve each two-step equation. Then, put the variables and their values in order from least to greatest to answer the riddle.

1. $2r + 15 = 33$

$r =$ _____

2. $13 = 3v - 8$

$v =$ _____

3. $2l + 4 = 30$

$l =$ _____

4. $6l - 1 = 17$

$l =$ _____

5. $2i - 8 = 12$

$i =$ _____

6. $5a + 9 = 64$

$a =$ _____

7. $3a - 9 = 15$

$a =$ _____

8. $2l - 3 = 5$

$l =$ _____

9. $3e + 5 = 47$

$e =$ _____

10. $31 + 5b = 56$

$b =$ _____

11. $10b - 2 = 118$

$b =$ _____

12. $15 = 11 + 2t$

$t =$ _____

13. $4 + 2e = 16$

$e =$ _____

14. $12i - 7 = 5$

$i =$ _____

What did x say when y asked about the weather?

Order the values of the variables from least to greatest:

___ ___ ___ ___   ___ ___   ___ ___ ___ ___ ___ ___ ___

Variables:

___ ___ ___ ___   ___ ___   ___ ___ ___ ___ ___ ___ ___

Name _____

Inequality Intersections

For inequalities involving < or ≤, find the six greatest integer solutions.
For inequalities involving > or ≥, find the six least integer solutions. Then,
place the solutions of the inequalities in the Venn diagram. (If an inequality
has fewer than six integer solutions, place all of its integer solutions.)

1. $a > 5$ $b \leq 8$

2. $x \geq 6$ $y < 4$

3. $m \leq 9$ $n > 3$

4. $p \leq 20$ $q \geq 17$

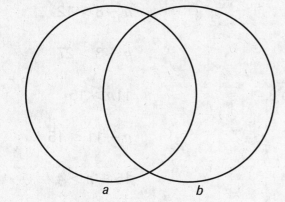

5. $f < 9$ $3 < g \leq 9$
"3 is less than g,
and g is less than
or equal to 9"

6. $4 \leq c < 10$ $8 > d \geq 4$
"4 is less than or   "8 is greater than
equal to c, and c is d, and d is greater
less than 10"   than or equal to 4"

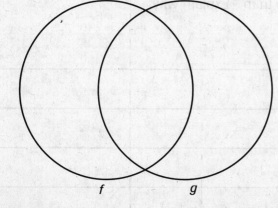

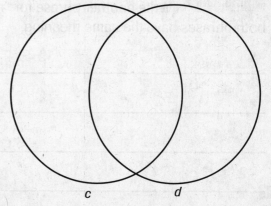

Words and Symbols

Match the word sentence with the corresponding inequality.

1. 3 more than a number is greater than 27. $7n \leq 14$

2. 15 more than a number is greater than 4. $n - 12 \geq 8$

3. 8 less than a number is more than 12. $n - 8 > 12$

4. 7 times a number is at most 14. $n + 3 > 27$

5. 12 less than a number is greater than or equal to 8. $11n > 15$

6. 12 times a number is less than or equal to 36. $n - 11 \leq 15$

7. 11 less than a number is no more than 15. $15 + n > 4$

8. 15 more than a number is no less than 4. $12n \leq 36$

9. 3 times a number is no more than 27. $3n \leq 27$

10. 11 times a number is greater than 15. $n + 15 \geq 4$

11. 7 less than a number is at most 14. $3 + n < 27$

12. 8 times a number is greater than or equal to 12. $n - 7 \leq 14$

13. 3 more than a number is less than 27. $12n < 36$

14. 12 times a number is less than 36. $8n \geq 12$

15. **Write Math** Write another phrase for "no more than." Explain why both phrases have the same meaning.

_____

_____

_____

Inequalities on the Number Line

Use addition, subtraction, multiplication, or division to get the variable by itself. Then, match the inequality with the correct number line. Be sure to perform the same operation on both sides of the inequality.

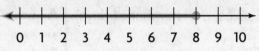

Number Line A

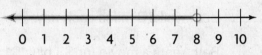

Number Line B

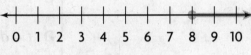

Number Line C

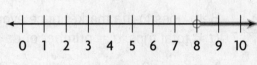

Number Line D

1. $y + 7 \geq 15$

Solve: _____

Number Line: _____

2. $h - 5 \leq 3$

Solve: _____

Number Line: _____

3. $\dfrac{g}{4} < 2$

Solve: _____

Number Line: _____

4. $2z > 16$

Solve: _____

Number Line: _____

5. Stretch Your Thinking Solve and graph the inequality.

$n - 6\frac{1}{9} \leq 2\frac{2}{3}$

_____

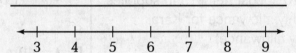

6. ▶Write Math▶ Write three numerical solutions to the inequality for Problem 5. Explain why they are solutions.

_____

_____

_____

What's My Equation?

Each set of equations uses the same variables. For each situation, write the letter for its equation.

1. ___ Beth walks 3 miles each day. (t = total miles, d = number of days)

    ___ Beth rents a movie for $3 plus $1 per day.
(t = total cost, d = number of days)

    ___ Beth goes to the market once every 3 days.
(t = total trips, d = number of days)

    ___ Terence is 3 years younger than Diana. (t = Terence's age in years, d = Diana's age in years)

A $t = d - 3$

B $t = d + 3$

C $t = 3d$

D $t = d \div 3$

2. ___ Jon and 3 friends each pay the same amount for dinner.
(c = each person's cost, p = total price of dinner)

    ___ Jon gets a $4 discount on the price of a shirt.
(c = final cost, p = initial price of shirt)

    ___ Jon pays $4 shipping charge in addition to the price of a video game. (c = final cost, p = price before shipping)

    ___ Jon buys 4 DVDs of equal price. (c = final cost, p = price of 1 DVD)

A $c = 4p$

B $c = p \div 4$

C $c = p - 4$

D $c = p + 4$

3. ___ Kara's uncle deposits $40 into her college savings account each month starting on her next birthday, and will start the account with 15 months' worth of deposits. (t = total savings, m = number of months)

    ___ Kara's karate membership includes a $15 startup fee and then $40 per month. ($t$ = total cost, m = number of months)

    ___ Kara sells one of her paintings for $40. It cost her $15 in supplies. The profit is split equally into a monthly allowance for Kara. (m = number of months, t = monthly allowance)

    ___ The tree in Kara's front yard grows 40 inches every 15 months. (t = total growth in inches, m = number of months)

A $t = \dfrac{40 - 15}{m}$

B $t = 40(m + 15)$

C $t = 40\left(\dfrac{m}{15}\right)$

D $t = 40m + 15$

Write Math ▸ Describe how you chose the equation for the first situation in Exercise 3. _____

_____

_____

Cellular Phone Relationships

Josie is deciding on a calling plan for her new cell phone.
She can choose from the four monthly calling plans below.
Write an equation to show the relationship for each plan.

Plan A

Minutes, m	Monthly Charge, c
1	$20.15
2	$20.30
3	$20.45
4	$20.60

Plan B

Minutes, m	Monthly Charge, c
5	$6.50
10	$8.00
15	$9.50
20	$11.00

_____

Plan C

Minutes, m	Monthly Charge, c
10	$4.50
20	$9.00
30	$13.50
40	$18.00

Plan D

Minutes, m	Monthly Charge, c
20	$11.00
30	$16.50
40	$22.00
50	$27.50

_____

Match each company below with their plan.

1. Company Xenon charges $0.45 per minute.

   Plan: _____

2. Pythagorean Cellular charges $20 per month and $0.15 per minute.

   Plan: _____

3. Aztec Phone charges $0.55 per minute.

   Plan: _____

4. Triangular Wireless charges $0.30 per minute and a monthly $5 satellite fee.

   Plan: _____

5. **Stretch Your Thinking** Josie talks on the phone for an average of 50 minutes per month. Which plan is the cheapest for Josie?

   _____

6. **Stretch Your Thinking** Which plan is the most expensive for a month in which Josie makes no calls?

   _____

Name _____

See the Pattern

Write an equation for the pattern. Then fill in the unknown quantity.

1. Suzy is studying for next year's Super Student Spelling Bee.

Suzy's Spelling Study				
Days, d	17	121	205	365
Words, w	102	726	1,230	

Equation: _____

2. Ferris is in charge of serving dinner to the dogs at Darling Doggie Daycare.

Darling Doggie Dog Dinner				
Dogs, d	3	7	11	36
Cups, c	$4\frac{1}{2}$	$10\frac{1}{2}$	$16\frac{1}{2}$	

Equation: _____

3. Mr. Painter orders art supplies for his students.

Mr. Painter's Art Supplies					
Students, s	7	18		165	320
Dollars, d	84	216	360	1,980	3,840

Equation: _____

4. Kat knits the same number of inches per hour.

Kat's Knitting					
Hours, h	3	8	12	15	32
Inches, i	$5\frac{1}{4}$	14		$26\frac{1}{4}$	56

Equation: _____

5. The Happy Coffee Café orders coffee by the pound.

Happy Coffee Café's Coffee				
Pounds, p	5	9	12	30
Dollars, d	12	21.60	28.80	

Equation: _____

6. The Safe-T-First Trucking Team averages the same number of miles each hour.

Safe-T-First Trucking Team's Travel					
Hours, h	$1\frac{1}{3}$	$4\frac{1}{2}$	$5\frac{2}{3}$	$6\frac{1}{2}$	
Miles, m	60	$202\frac{1}{2}$	255	$292\frac{1}{2}$	315

Equation: _____

7. **Write Math** ➤ How could you use your equation from Exercise 5 to find the cost of 15 pounds of coffee? Explain your process and find the answer.

_____

_____

_____

What's My Line?

Draw a line that connects each table to the correct graph.

1.

x	2	4	6	8
y	1	2	3	4

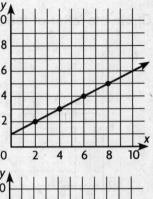

2.

x	4	5	6	7
y	9	8	7	6

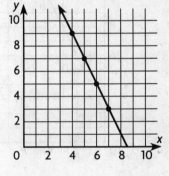

3.

x	2	4	6	8
y	2	3	4	5

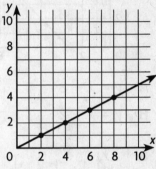

4.

x	6	7	8	9
y	6	7	8	9

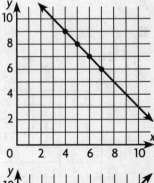

5.

x	4	5	6	7
y	9	7	5	3

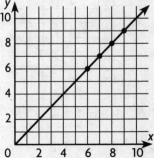

Name _____

Straight to the Equation

Circle the letter of the correct equation for each graph.

1.

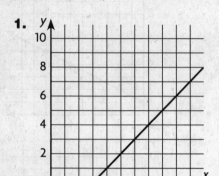

A $y = x + 3$ **C** $y = x - 3$

B $y = x + 2$ **D** $y = x - 2$

2.

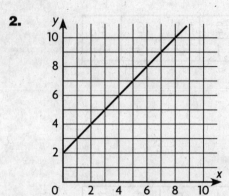

A $y = x + 2$ **C** $y = x - 2$

B $y = x + 1$ **D** $y = x - 1$

3.

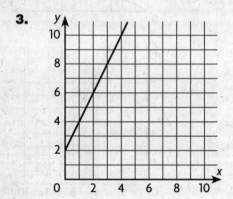

A $y = x + 2$ **C** $y = x - 2$

B $y = 2x + 2$ **D** $y = 2x - 2$

4.

A $y = 3x + 2$ **C** $y = 3x - 2$

B $y = 3x + 1$ **D** $y = 3x - 1$

5.

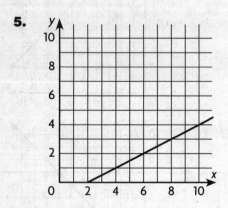

A $y = \frac{1}{2}x + 1$ **C** $y = \frac{1}{2}x - 1$

B $y = \frac{1}{2}x + 2$ **D** $y = \frac{1}{2}x - 2$

6.

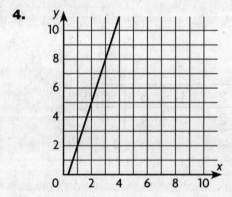

A $y = \frac{1}{3}x + 1$ **C** $y = \frac{1}{3}x - 1$

B $y = \frac{1}{3}x + 2$ **D** $y = \frac{1}{3}x - 2$

All Aboard Parallelogram and Square Express

Find the areas of the train cars below. Write the shape of the car and the formula you used to find the area. (Do not include the wheels as part of the area.)

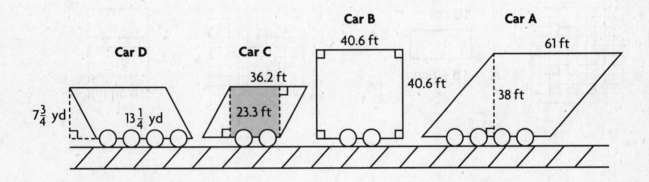

Train Car A	Train Car B
Figure: _____	Figure: _____
Formula for the Area: _____	Formula for the Area: _____
Area: _____	Area: _____
Train Car C	**Train Car D**
Figure: _____	Figure: _____
Formula for the Area: _____	Formula for the Area: _____
Area: _____	Area: _____

1. **Stretch Your Thinking** Add another car to the train. Draw and label the car. Then find the area.

2. **Stretch Your Thinking** If the unshaded triangles in Train Car C are removed, the figure is a square. What is the area of the shaded section of Train Car C?

_____   _____

Tricky Triangles

Find the missing base or height of the first triangle in each
problem. Draw the triangle on the grid to help you visualize your
answer. Then, on the other grid, draw another triangle
with the same area but a different base and height.

1.

$b = 10$ cm

$h = $ [　　　]

$A = 15$ sq cm

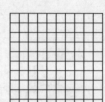

$b = $ [　　　]

$h = $ [　　　]

$A = 15$ sq cm

2.

$b = $ [　　　]

$h = 2$ cm

$A = 6$ sq cm

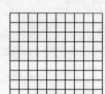

$b = $ [　　　]

$h = $ [　　　]

$A = 6$ sq cm

3.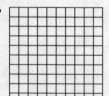

$b = $ [　　　]

$h = 4$ cm

$A = 8$ sq cm

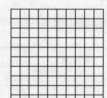

$b = $ [　　　]

$h = $ [　　　]

$A = 8$ sq cm

4.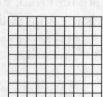

$b = 8$ cm

$h = $ [　　　]

$A = 12$ sq cm

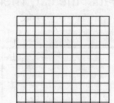

$b = $ [　　　]

$h = $ [　　　]

$A = 12$ sq cm

Wordy Triangles

Make a drawing to show the situation. Label the dimensions. Then use the drawing to find the area.

1. A model ship has a mast that is 7 inches tall. A right triangular sail goes from the top of the mast to 1 inch from the bottom of the mast. The length of the base of the sail is 4 inches. The height of the sail is along the mast.

Area of sail: _____

2. Two ropes extend from the top of a flagpole to the ground 18 feet away from the flagpole's base on either side. The flagpole is 30 feet high. The ropes each create a right triangle with the flagpole, and each right triangle is half of a larger triangle with the flagpole at its center.

Area of larger triangle: _____

3. Andrew is helping the first-grade class make paper trees. For each student, he folds a rectangular piece of construction paper in half lengthwise. Then, he cuts the folded paper into a triangular shape with the same base and height as the rectangle. Then he unfolds the paper and throws away the scraps. The original piece of paper is 11 inches by 8.5 inches.

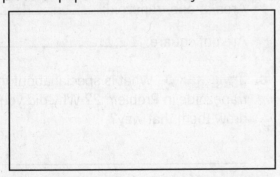

Area of paper thrown away per student:

_____

4. Lucy's rectangular garden is 15 feet long and 12 feet wide. She adds a right triangle to her garden plan, so that the triangle's height extends out 7 feet in line with the shorter side of the rectangle, and the base of the triangle runs from the corner of the rectangle to the center of the longer side of the rectangle.

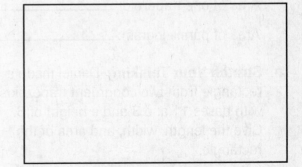

Total area of Lucy's garden:

_____

Name _____

Trapezoid Patterns

Use the grid to draw each polygon.
Label the measurements and give the areas.

1. Hexagon made from two congruent trapezoids with bases 4 and 6 and height 2

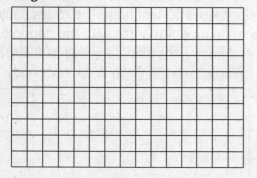

Area of one trapezoid: _____

Area of hexagon: _____

2. Rectangle made from two congruent trapezoids with bases 5 and 7 and height 3

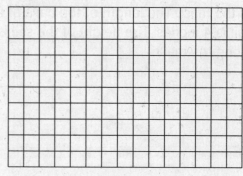

Area of one trapezoid: _____

Area of rectangle: _____

3. Parallelogram made from two congruent trapezoids with bases 3 and 8 and height 5

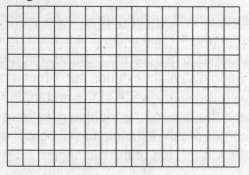

Area of one trapezoid: _____

Area of parallelogram: _____

4. Square made from four congruent trapezoids with bases 5 and 3 and height 4

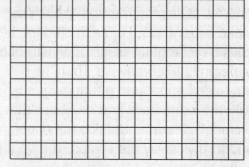

Area of one trapezoid: _____

Area of square: _____

5. **Stretch Your Thinking** Daniel made a rectangle from two congruent trapezoids with bases 11 and 8 and a height of 6. Give the length, width, and area of the rectangle.

6. **Write Math** ▸ What is special about the trapezoids in Problem 2? Why did you draw them that way?

_____

_____

_____

Split into Two

A trapezoid can be divided into two triangles. Label each triangle
with its height and base. Then find the area of the triangles and the
area of the trapezoid.

1.

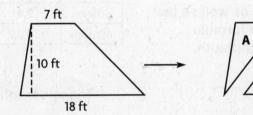

Areas

Triangle A: _____

Triangle B: _____

Trapezoid: _____

2.

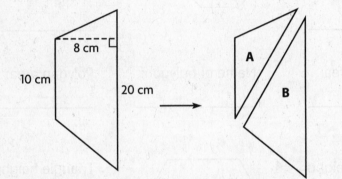

Areas

Triangle A: _____

Triangle B: _____

Trapezoid: _____

3.

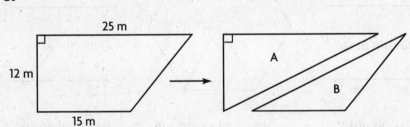

Areas

Triangle A: _____

Triangle B: _____

Trapezoid: _____

4. **Write Math** ▸ The formula for the area of a trapezoid is
$A = \frac{1}{2}(b_1 + b_2)h$. Rewrite the formula as the sum of the areas
of two triangles. Which properties did you use to rewrite the formula?

_____

_____

_____

Off on a Tangent

You can find the approximate height of a triangle inside a regular polygon by using a tangent, the ratio of the triangle's height, h, to half the polygon's side length, s: $\frac{h}{s \div 2}$.

Find the approximate height and area for the triangle, as well as the area of the polygon. Use the table of tangents and the formula $h = \tan \times (s \div 2)$. Round each value to the nearest hundredth.

Polygon	Tangent (tan)
pentagon	1.38
hexagon	1.73
octagon	2.41
decagon	3.08

1.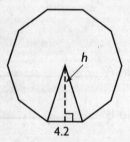

10

Triangle height:

_____

Triangle area:

_____

Name of polygon:

_____

Polygon area:

_____

2.

9.1

Triangle height:

_____

Triangle area:

_____

Name of polygon:

_____

Polygon area:

_____

3.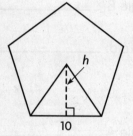

4.2

Triangle height:

_____

Triangle area:

_____

Name of polygon:

_____

Polygon area:

_____

4.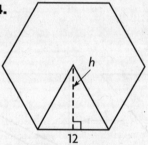

12

Triangle height:

_____

Triangle area:

_____

Name of polygon:

_____

Polygon area:

_____

5. Stretch Your Thinking Bethany says she can draw a regular hexagon with side length 16 and triangle height 11. Is this possible? How can you tell?

_____

_____

Find Areas of Composite Figures

Solve.

1. A skateboard ramp is made of the figures as shown. What is the area of the front of the ramp?

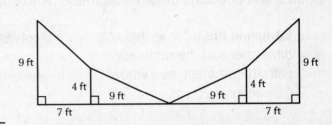

_____

2. A bean bag game wall is shown. Each hole in the wall is in the shape of a square with side length 3 inches. What is the area of the wall, without counting the holes?

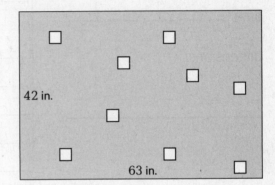

_____

3. **Stretch Your Thinking** Mr. Siers is building an entrance to the front of his ranch, as shown. What is the area of the front of the entrance?

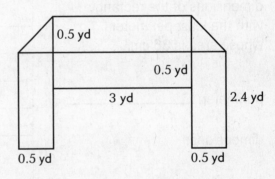

_____

4. **Write Math** ▶ How is finding the area of a parallelogram like finding the area of two congruent triangles? Explain your answer.

_____

_____

_____

_____

_____

Fixing Perimeter and Area

You have explored how changing the dimensions of a polygon affects
the area. Now you will explore what happens when you fix the perimeter
or area and allow the other measurements to change.

1. Complete the table to find the
dimensions of the rectangle
with the greatest area whose
perimeter is 20 cm.

area: _____

dimensions:

_____

Length (cm)	Width (cm)	Perimeter (cm)	Area (cm²)
9	1	20	9
8	2	20	
7			
6			
5			
4			
3			
2			
1			

2. Complete the table to find the
dimensions of the rectangle
with the least perimeter
whose area is 36 cm².

perimeter: _____

dimensions:

_____

Length (cm)	Width (cm)	Perimeter (cm)	Area (cm²)
1	36	74	36
2	18		36
3			
4			
6			
9			
12			
18			
36			

3. **Stretch Your Thinking** What can you
conclude about the dimensions of a
rectangle with a fixed perimeter?

_____

_____

_____

4. **Stretch Your Thinking** What can you
conclude about the dimensions of a
rectangle with a fixed area?

_____

_____

_____

Hidden Picture

Use the clues to find the missing vertices. Plot the missing vertices on the coordinate grid and draw each quadrilateral to complete the picture below.

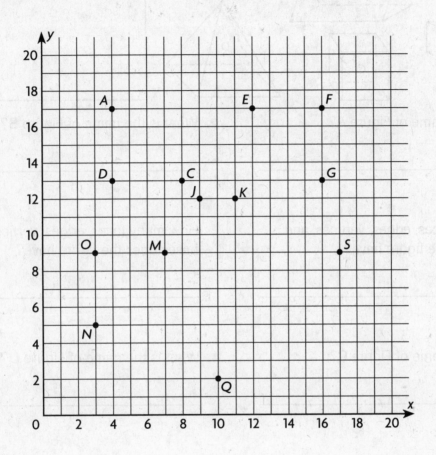

CLUES:

1. *ABCD* is a rectangle.

2. *EFGH* is a square.

3. *JKLM* is a trapezoid, and $\overline{LM}$ is 6 units long

4. *NOPQ* and *PQRS* are parallelograms.

Point *B*: _____

Point *H*: _____

Point *L*: _____

Point *P*: _____

Point *R*: _____

Solid Identification

Use the figures below to answer the questions.

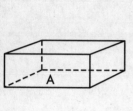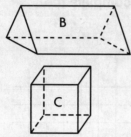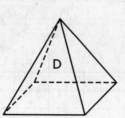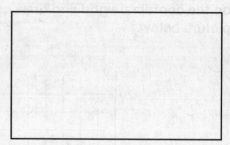

1. What is the name of Figure A?

_____

How many faces, edges, vertices, and bases does the figure have?

_____

2. What is the name of Figure B?

_____

How many faces, edges, vertices, and bases does the figure have?

_____

3. What is the name of Figure C?

_____

How many faces, edges, vertices, and bases does the figure have?

_____

4. What is the name of Figure D?

_____

How many faces, edges, vertices, and bases does the figure have?

_____

5. Stretch Your Thinking Draw a triangular pyramid in the rectangle at the top of the page.

How many faces, edges, vertices, and bases does the figure have?

_____

_____

6. **Write Math** Describe the similarities and differences between a triangular prism and a rectangular prism.

_____

_____

Nets, Nets, Nets

Draw and label two nets for the rectangular prism. Then use the nets to find the surface area.

1. length 9 cm

width 3 cm

height 5 cm

Surface area: _____

2. length 4 in.

width 6 in.

height 2 in.

Surface area: _____

3. length 7.3 m

width 3.2 m

height 8.5 m

Surface area: _____

Use Surface Area to Make Food Packages

You've been hired to design packaging for the following food items. Match each box with its description. Then find the surface area of the indicated material.

Item: Green Energy Tea Bags The tea is sold in a 9.5 in. cubic box fully lined with tissue paper. Box: _____ Tissue paper area: _____	**Item: Country Cabin Corn** The box has length 14.5 in., width 9.2 in., and height 5 in. The box is wrapped in two layers of freezer paper. Box: _____ Total paper area: _____
Item: Tasty Flakes and Raisins Cereal The top and bottom of the cereal box is 10 in. by 2.5 in. The box is 12.3 in. high. The cardboard is coated with dye, except on the bottom. Box: _____ Dyed area: _____	**Item: V.I.P. Select Chocolates** Two boxes are stacked and tied with a ribbon. Each box is fully wrapped in decorative paper. Bottom box: $8 \times 6 \times 3$ in. Top box: $5 \times 3 \times 2$ in. Box: _____ Total paper area: _____

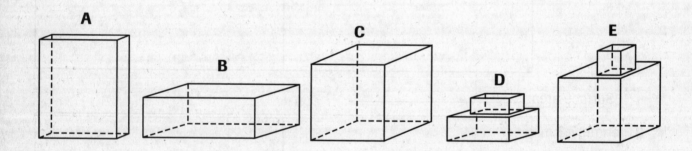

1. **Stretch Your Thinking** Tissue paper for the tea boxes costs $0.01 per square inch. How much would it cost to line a dozen boxes, to the nearest penny?

_____

_____

_____

2. **Write Math** Green Tea decided they do not want tissue paper on the top of the box. Using the surface area you found, explain how to find the new surface area.

_____

_____

_____

Surface Formulas

Draw and label a net for the solid figure. Then use the net to
write an algebraic formula for the surface area.

Apply your formula using the given values.

1. Rectangular prism

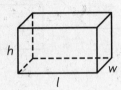

Net

2 (_____) + 2 (_____) + 2 (_____)

Evaluate for $l = 5$ in., $w = 3$ in., $h = 4$ in. _____

2. Triangular pyramid; faces and base have the
same measurements

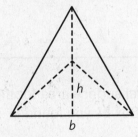

Net

_____

Evaluate for $b = 6$ ft and $h = 5.2$ ft. _____

3. Write Math ➤ How would the formula for surface area of a triangular pyramid be different if
the base and other faces were not equivalent?

_____

_____

_____

Name _____

Packing Boxes

Sometimes products are less expensive when
bought in larger packages. Have you ever
wondered why?

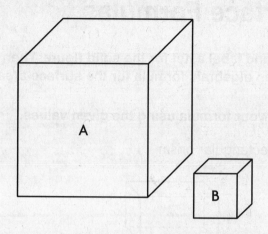

1. Box A is a cube with a side length of
$1\frac{1}{2}$ inches.

    a. Find the surface area of the box.

_____

    b. Find the volume of the box.

_____

2. Box B is a cube with a side length of
$\frac{1}{2}$ inch.

    a. Find the surface area of the box.

_____

    b. Find the volume of the box.

_____

3. How many of Box B would it take to
fill Box A?

_____

4. Find the total surface area for the
number of Box Bs you found in
Problem 3.

_____

5. Which has a smaller surface area, Box A, or multiple Box Bs?

_____

6. **Write Math** ▸ The company pays for boxes according to how many square inches of
cardboard each box uses. Which is less expensive to use, Box A or multiple Box Bs?
How do you know?

_____

_____

Aquarium Volumes on Display

A pet store is selling aquariums. You have been asked to find
the volumes of the aquariums in cubic inches. After finding
the volumes, answer the questions that follow.

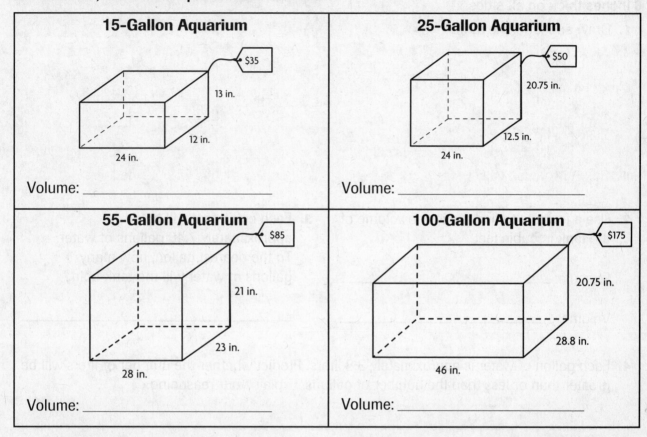

15-Gallon Aquarium

$35

13 in.

12 in.

24 in.

Volume: _____

25-Gallon Aquarium

$50

20.75 in.

12.5 in.

24 in.

Volume: _____

55-Gallon Aquarium

$85

21 in.

23 in.

28 in.

Volume: _____

100-Gallon Aquarium

$175

20.75 in.

28.8 in.

46 in.

Volume: _____

1. A customer says he has a rectangular
aquarium with a length of 37 in., a width
of 19 in., and a height of 19 in. What is
the volume of the aquarium?

_____

2. The gallon sizes above are approximate.
To which size is the customer's aquarium
closest?

_____

3. Stretch Your Thinking What is the volume of the 25-gallon aquarium in *cubic feet*?
Round to the nearest tenth.

_____

4. Write Math ▶ Which of the four aquariums has the best value, based on the advertised
gallon sizes? Explain your answer.

_____

_____

_____

Volume at the Aquarium

The County Aquarium has some new exhibits. The Shark Tank is a closed aquarium that has a length of 732 inches, a width of 420 inches, and a height of 144 inches. The glass is 6 inches thick on all sides.

1. Draw and label the tank.

2. Use a formula to find the inside volume of the tank in cubic feet.

Formula: _____

Volume: _____

3. Each cubic foot will hold approximately 7.48 gallons of water. To the nearest gallon, how many gallons of water will the tank hold?

_____

4. Each gallon of water is approximately 3.8 liters. Predict whether the number of liters will be greater than or less than the number of gallons. Explain your reasoning.

_____

_____

5. To the nearest liter, how many liters of water does the shark tank hold?

_____

6. **Write Math** Explain why you can or cannot figure out the shape of a tank if you only know how many gallons it holds.

_____

_____

_____

Questions and Conclusions

Look at each data set, and give a statistical question that
might have been asked about the extremes of the data.
For example, what is the highest number of cars sold?
Then, based on the data in the table, answer your question.

1.

Classmates' Allergies

3	0	1	0
0	0	4	6
2	0	0	2
0	2	5	0
7	3	0	1

Question: _____

_____

Answer: _____

2.

Average Precipitation

Chicago, IL		Phoenix, AZ	
Month	Inches	Month	Inches
Jan.	1.8	Jan.	0.8
March	2.7	March	1.1
May	3.4	May	0.1
July	3.5	July	0.9
Sept.	3.3	Sept.	0.8
Nov.	3.0	Nov.	0.7

Question: _____

_____

_____

Answer: _____

3.

**Percentage of Correct
Crossword Puzzle Words**

Ethan			Jacob		
70	95	99	75	60	55
60	75	80	90	35	40
80	100	75	65	95	80

Question: _____

_____

_____

Answer: _____

4. **Write Math** ▶ Explain what makes your questions statistical.

_____

_____

_____

_____

Be the Researcher

Design your own studies! For each study, choose the attribute, the unit, and the means of measurement from the table, and decide how many observations to include. Make sure that the attribute, the unit, and the means go together. Then, describe your study in a sentence.

For the third study, think of a statistical question you could ask, and then complete the design of the study.

Attributes	Units	Means
time	grams	yardstick
number	minutes	ruler
weight	ounces	balance
length	number	clock
mass	centimeters	counting
height	feet	scale

1. Statistical question: How tall are my 18 classmates?

Attribute:
height

Units:

_____

Means:
yardstick

Observations:

_____

Description: _____

_____

2. Statistical question: How much does the food in 4 of my dinners weigh?

Attribute:

_____

Units:
ounces

Means:

_____

Observations:
4

Description: _____

_____

_____

3. Statistical question: _____

_____

Attribute:

_____

Units:

_____

Means:

_____

Observations:

_____

Description: _____

_____

Serving Up Dot Plots and Frequency Tables

Use the space to the right to make a dot plot or relative frequency table of the data.

1. The table below shows the number of tables Marisa served at a restaurant.

Number of Tables Served Daily

8	9	13	12	9
11	8	4	8	11
8	12	7	10	9
9	10	12	8	13
13	7	11	9	10

Make a dot plot of the data.

2. What number(s) of tables did Marisa serve most often?

_____

3. What number(s) of tables did Marisa serve least often?

_____

4. The tally chart shows the number of days Marisa worked different hours.

Daily Hours Marisa Worked

Whole Number of Hours Worked	Tally
0–2 h	II
3–4 h	IIII
5–6 h	HHT III
7–8 h	HHT HHT I

Make a relative frequency table of the data.

5. Stretch Your Thinking How many days did Marisa work 6 hours or less?

_____

6. How many days did Marisa work 4 hours or less?

_____

7. Write Math ▸ How do dot plots and frequency tables show data differently?

_____

_____

Name _____

Plotting Along the Beach

Lifeguards at Stony Beach were told to record data
on visitors to the beach one morning. They made the
following tables below based on their results.

Ages of Swimmers

12	45	11	65	31	8
38	17	59	5	21	16
68	52	12	3	24	15
16	35	5	9	67	23
25	7	13	19	21	5

Money in Dollars Spent per Family at Refreshment and Souvenir Stands

13	6	25	18	10	29
5	14	15	23	34	9
16	52	26	12	7	38
13	25	31	20	5	6
34	8	11	29	22	30

**Make a histogram for the ages of swimmers
at the beach for that morning.**

**Make a frequency table for the number
of dollars spent per family at the beach.**

1. **Stretch Your Thinking** How many more
   swimmers at the beach were 10–19 years
   old than were 40–49 years old?

2. How many families spent $10–$19 at the
   beach?

_____

_____

3. **Write Math** ▸ Explain how histograms and frequency tables are similar
   and how they are different.

_____

_____

Dotty for Data

Complete the dot plot for the data. Check distances
to see if the suggested mean is the correct balance point.

1. **Rings on Stumps in Shady Forest**

32	34	52	40
39	29	40	

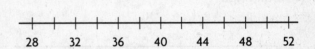

Suggested mean: 45

Total distance for lesser values: _____

Total distance for greater values: _____

Is the mean correct? _____

2. **Mass of Emma's Books (kg)**

Reading	1.4	Math	1.3
Writing	0.6	Science	0.9
Social Studies	1.3	Music	1.1

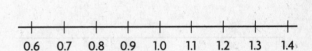

Suggested mean: 1.1

Total distance for lesser values: _____

Total distance for greater values: _____

Is the mean correct? _____

3. **Ages of Stuart's Cousins**

$12\frac{1}{2}$	6	$12\frac{1}{2}$	17	$4\frac{1}{2}$
11	13	6	$15\frac{1}{2}$	12

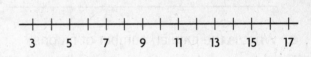

Suggested mean: 11

Total distance for lesser values: _____

Total distance for greater values: _____

Is the mean correct? _____

4. **Write Math** ▶ Is the mean in Problem 1 greater than or less than the suggested mean?
Explain how you know without calculating it.

_____

_____

_____

_____

Numbers In and Out of This World

Use the tables to answer the questions.

1. What is the mean height of the buildings?

_____

2. What is the mode?

_____

3. What is the median height of the buildings?

_____

4. What is the mean number of moons?

_____

5. What is the mode?

_____

6. What is the median number of moons?

_____

Tallest Buildings by Country

Country	Height of Tallest Building (in feet)
Spain	820
Nigeria	272
Morocco	377
Austria	663
Bolivia	351
Finland	282
Peru	351
South Africa	732

Number of Known Planetary Moons

Planet	Number of Moons
Mercury	0
Venus	0
Earth	1
Mars	2
Jupiter	63
Saturn	34
Uranus	27
Neptune	13

7. Stretch Your Thinking If El Salvador is added to the table for Tallest Buildings by Country, the median height would be 367 feet. How tall is the tallest building in El Salvador?

_____

8. **Write Math** ➤ Did you get a decimal answer for Problems 4–6? Explain how an answer can be a decimal. (There's no such thing as 0.5 moons.)

_____

_____

Grading the Test

Make a dot plot for the scores. Find the mean with and without the outlier, to the nearest tenth. Describe the effect of the outlier.

1. **Quiz: 20 questions**
   Scores: 16, 20, 15, 8, 19, 20, 18,
   17, 16, 15, 16, 14, 16, 17

   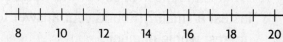

   Mean with outlier: Outlier: Mean without outlier:

   _____   _____   _____

   The outlier _____

2. **Quiz: 50 questions**
   Scores: 30, 15, 18, 17, 16, 24, 21, 48,
   24, 33, 18, 16, 31, 18, 31

   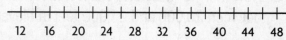

   Mean with outlier: Outlier: Mean without outlier:

   _____   _____   _____

   The outlier _____

3. **Test: 100 questions**
   Scores: 86, 99, 82, 78, 83,
   86, 83, 79, 78, 86

   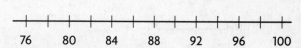

   Mean with outlier: Outlier: Mean without outlier:

   _____   _____   _____

   The outlier _____

4. **Stretch Your Thinking** Using the mean without
   the outlier, calculate the mean score for Problem 1 as a percent.

   _____

5. **Write Math** ▶ Why would it be useful for a teacher to remove outliers
   before calculating the mean for an exam?

   _____

   _____

Name That Graph!

**Identify the graph on the right that goes with the question on the left.
Use the question to fill in the missing information on the graph.
Then, use the graph to answer the question.**

1. What is the mean speed of the world's
fastest animals? (Round your answer to the
nearest whole number.)

Graph: _____

Answer: _____

A.
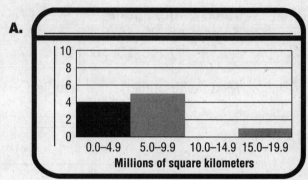

2. How many of the world's tallest mountains are
between 20,000 and 21,900 feet in elevation?

Graph: _____

Answer: _____

B.
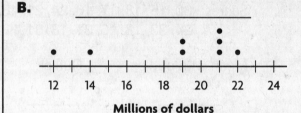

3. How many countries are between 0 and
4.9 million square kilometers in area?

Graph: _____

Answer: _____

C.
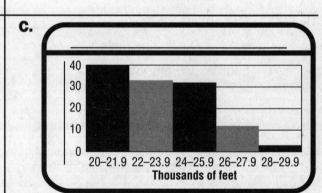

4. What is the median amount of dollars spent
for the highest spending states?

Graph: _____

Answer: _____

D.
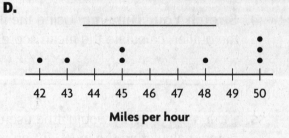

5. **Write Math** ► How did you determine which graph went with Problem 2?

_____

_____

Peaks and Valleys

Complete the dot plot or histogram to match the indicated characteristics.

1. Decreases then increases, no symmetry

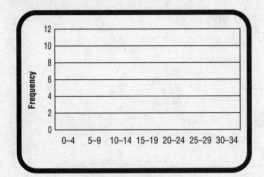

2. Three gaps

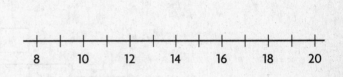

3. One peak, no symmetry

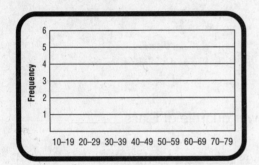

4. Two peaks, symmetry

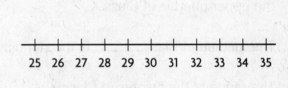

5. Two gaps, symmetry

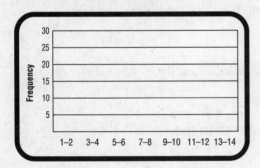

6. Two clusters

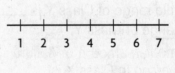

7. **Stretch Your Thinking** Describe any other characteristics that the histogram in Exercise 1 has.

_____

_____

_____

Double Box Talk

Stacking box plots one above the other on the same number line can be very useful when comparing two sets of data.

The heights (in inches) of students in two math classes are shown in the double-box plot. Complete each statement.

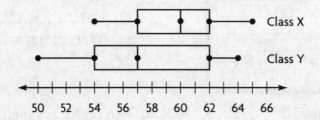

1. The upper quartile of Class Y is _____ inches. This is _____ the upper quartile of Class X.

2. The median of Class _____ is the same as the lower quartile of Class _____.

3. The range of the heights in Class X is _____ inches _____ than the range of the heights in Class Y.

4. The minimum value in Class _____ is the same as the _____ of Class Y.

5. The interquartile range of Class Y is _____ the interquartile range of Class Y.

6. The shortest person in Class X is _____ inches taller than the

   shortest person in Class _____.

7. **Write Math** ▸ Describe what information you cannot gather about a data set from its box plot.

   _____

   _____

   _____

Circling the Mean

The mean and 7 values of an 8-value data set are given
in the middle circle. An 8th value and the mean absolute
deviation (MAD) are given in each of the four smaller circles.
Choose the 8th value in the data set that will make the
mean and MAD correct.

1.

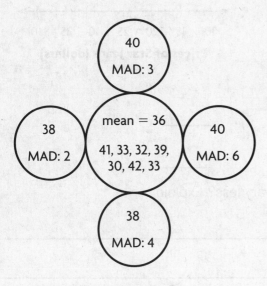

2.

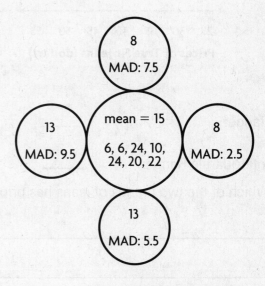

3.

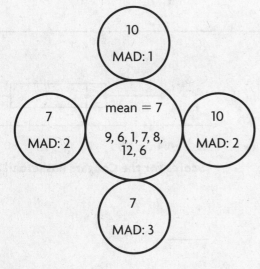

4.

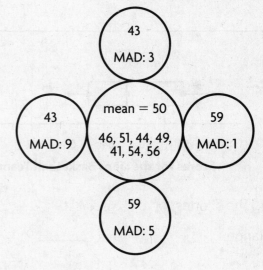

5. **Write Math** ▸ Explain how you determined the correct choice
for Exercise 1.

_____

_____

_____

Small by Comparison

Find the range and interquartile range. Then answer the question comparing the data sets.

1.

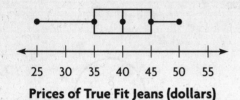

25 30 35 40 45 50 55
Prices of True Fit Jeans (dollars)

10 15 20 25 30 35 40
Prices of Star Jeans (dollars)

Range: _____   _____

Interquartile Range: _____   _____

Which of the two brands of jeans has prices that vary less? Explain.

_____

_____

_____

2.

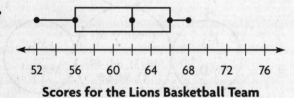

52 56 60 64 68 72 76
Scores for the Lions Basketball Team

60 64 68 72 76 80 84
Scores for the Cougars Basketball Team

Range: _____   _____

Interquartile Range: _____   _____

Which of the two teams has scores that vary more? Explain.

_____

_____

_____

Where Is the Data?

**Give a data set that meets the description. Each data set must
have at least 6 values. Explain why your data set is correct.**

1. The mean and median of lunch prices
best represent the data.

Mean: _____   Median: _____

_____   Explanation: _____

_____   _____

     _____

2. The mode of the number of pens in a
pack best represents the data.

Mode(s): _____

_____   Explanation: _____

_____   _____

     _____

3. The range of the quiz scores is a better
description of the data set than the
interquartile range.

Range: _____   Interquartile range: _____

Explanation: _____

_____   _____

_____   _____

     _____

4. The interquartile range of the Fahrenheit
temperatures is a better description of
the data set than the range.

Range: _____   Interquartile range: _____

Explanation: _____

_____   _____

_____   _____

     _____

Dinner Time

The dinner prices for several different restaurants are given in the table.

1. Find the mean and range of each data set. Complete the table.

Restaurant	Dinner Prices ($)	Mean ($)	Range ($)
Happy's	13, 11, 15, 7, 10, 12, 11, 17		
Hungry's	18, 16, 15, 19, 15, 20, 20, 17		
Good Eats	11, 13, 9, 8, 13, 11, 12		
Red Table	12, 9, 9, 11, 12, 10, 9, 12		

2. Two restaurants have dinners that have the same variation in pricing. However, one place has dinners that are typically more expensive and the other place has dinners that are less expensive. What are the restaurants?

   _____

3. Which two restaurants have dinners that typically cost the same, but one place has dinners that vary in price much more?

   _____

4. Which two restaurants have the greatest difference in mean price

   _____

5. Which two restaurants differ greatly in both average dinner price and range of prices?

   _____

6. **Stretch Your Thinking** Suppose Red Table added another $12 menu item. Would the mean, range, or both be affected?

   _____

   _____

   _____

Telling the Truth

For each histogram or dot plot, write two true statements and
one false statement about the distribution.

1.

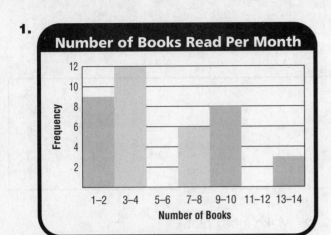

2.

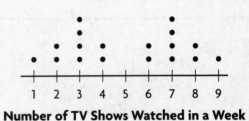

Number of TV Shows Watched in a Week

True statements:

_____

_____

_____

_____

True statements:

_____

_____

_____

_____

False statement:

_____

_____

False statement:

_____

_____

3. Stretch Your Thinking Find the mean, median, and
mode for the data set in Exercise 2. Which measure of center best
represents the data? Explain your answer.

_____

_____

_____

Am I Taller?

**Your friend claims that you are taller than most of your classmates.
Collect and record your height and your classmates' heights,
in inches.**

Classmates' Heights

_____

1. Complete the chart.

Lowest Height	
Highest Height	
Lower Quartile Height	
Median Height	
Upper Quartile Height	

2. Make a box plot.

3. Use the plot to draw a conclusion about your friend's claim.

_____

_____

_____

4. **Write Math** ▶ Calculate the mean of the heights. Is the
mean useful in making a conclusion about your friend's claim?
Explain why or why not.

_____

_____

_____